WRITINGS FROM

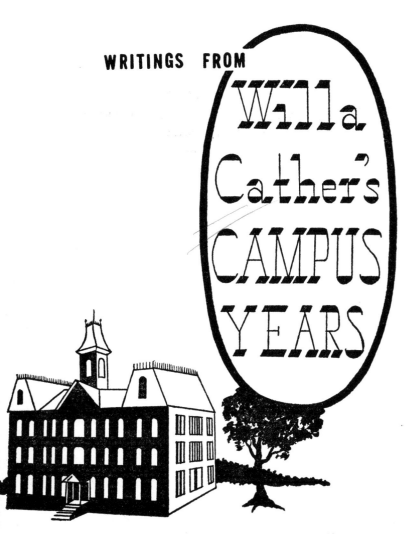

Willa Cather's CAMPUS YEARS

EDITED BY JAMES R SHIVELY

UNIVERSITY OF NEBRASKA PRESS

PS
3505
A87
A6

30577

Printed in the United States by
The Printing Division, University of Nebraska in Lincoln

Contents

Preface

The period of Willa Cather's life from 1890 to 1895, when she was a student at the University of Nebraska, has been almost completely ignored. It is an important and formative period in her life, however, for Miss Cather began to write seriously and extensively just at the time when she entered college and adult life. An examination of a distinguished author's first writings and early years is always rewarding, not only for the interest which the reading of juvenilia affords, but also for the aid it may give in determining the elusive qualities of the artist's talents and characteristics. This book, therefore, provides a representative collection of Willa Cather's early writings and reveals, as completely as possible, the person she was during her college years.

In making this study I have, of course, investigated the existing records of the university and of local and campus publications. More informative and important, I believe, have been the letters which I have received from many of Miss Cather's fellow students. These letters present such a delightfully revealing picture of the young Willa Cather and her university that I have, with the permission of their writers, included them in this volume.

Quotations pertaining to Stephen Crane and William Jennings Bryan are from articles by Willa Cather which originally appeared in the Library, *and recently were republished, in their entirety, in the* Prairie Schooner. *The works of Willa Cather reprinted in this volume were originally printed in newspapers and magazines, copies of which are now literary rarities. With the exception of the stories "Lou the Prophet" and "The Clemency of the Court," and the poems "Shakespeare, A Freshman Theme" and "Columbus," none of these writings have, to my knowledge, ever before been available to the general public.*

I am very grateful for information and assistance given to me by Miss Elsie Cather, Dr. Louise Pound, Miss Olivia Pound, Mrs. Mildred R. Bennett, Miss Emily Schossberger, Gaylord Marr, Professor Kenneth F. Forward, Dr. Walter F. Wright, *and, particularly,* Dr. Lowry C. Wimberly, *who suggested this investigation and publication, and guided me in its completion. Especially am I indebted, for her constant assistance, to* Ellen King Shively.

James R. Shively

February, 1950

WILLA CATHER IN 1893

Introduction

The Campus Years

Willa Cather was one of those persons who, once known, are always remembered. Today her college classmates recall her with feelings which vary from fervent admiration to vast contempt. Yet even after nearly sixty years none of them has forgotten her. From their letters and recollections there emerges a striking picture of the brilliant, eccentric girl who was to become one of America's great novelists.

The main source of her impressiveness could not have been her physical appearance alone, for in it there was little that was distinctive. She was of normal size, about five and a half feet in height, and somewhat stocky. Her clear complexion tended toward brunette, and her face, as one of her classmates described it, was "not one of doll–like beauty, but strong and good to look at."

If not her physical appearance, her startling disregard of current fashions made her unforgettable. Those were the 1890's, when the standard of feminine style, an elaborate fluffiness tempered with Victorian modesty, was so fixed as to make conspicuous any unconventionality of appearance. In such a period, Willa Cather appeared at the University of Nebraska with her hair "short and uncurled," cut in a "very stubby pompadour," and "shingled and parted on the side." Although she abandoned this startling coiffure during her sophomore year —she let her hair grow for her role as Lady Macbeth in a student theatrical production—she continued to dress in a manner which, for those times, was just as remarkable. Invariably she wore severely tailored suits with comparatively short skirts, shirt–type blouses with white starched fronts and linked cuffs, and usually a straw hat of a flat design; and one classmate said, "She was the first girl I ever saw in suspenders." Although her style of dress was noticeably, and perhaps intentionally, strange, it seems not really to have offended anyone, and the consensus of her fellow students is represented by one who said, "She was an individualist. Although boyish in her dress and at times in her mannerisms, she was never even inclined toward coarseness. On the other hand, she was not feminine in that she was not the type that apparently cared for lace and feminine finery."

It is quite understandable, of course, that a girl who undoubtedly cultivated a singular personality would not be remembered with unanimous admiration. It has been said of Willa Cather that she was "very egotistical" and "indifferent to other people," and that "she had no friends and wanted none." However, these opinions cannot be accepted unqualifiedly in face of the many descriptions of her as "courteous," "affable," "alert," and "vivacious"; and the memories of her "cheerful grin" and "hearty laugh." The truth seems to be that, conscious already of her unquestionably remarkable abilities, she was self-confident and rather assertive, and perhaps a little lonely.

That she had some good friends cannot be questioned, and although her circle of companions was small and of her own selection, there is a tone of at least grudging respect and often of genuine admiration in what her fellow students have said about her. Evidently sensing in Willa Cather that dedication to her own objectives which characterized her entire career, they sometimes misunderstood it as aloofness and egotism. One of her classmates said, "She was a girl that I very much liked and respected but I would hardly say that she was a girl that I was fond of, if you get the minor distinction." He probably expressed adequately the attitude of her associates toward Willa Cather.

As a student she was talented and inquiring, but erratic. Although records of grades earned during those years have not been preserved, apparently she was brilliant in subjects which interested her, and furiously impatient with those she considered unimportant. Excelling in languages and literature, she was incompetent in mathematics. It is difficult, in any event, to evaluate her scholarly ability because, for one thing, her age at the time is not known with certainty. The question would be of little importance except that it does affect one's impression not only of her ability as a student, but also of the writing she did in college.

She first entered the preparatory school at the University of Nebraska in September, 1890, at the age of only thirteen, if her customarily published birth date—December 7, 1876—is accepted. That it is not correct, however, is indicated by several circumstances. *Who's Who in America* originally listed the date as December 7, 1875, and did not change the year to 1876 until its issue of 1920–21. The fragmentary Register of Births in Frederick County, Virginia, where she was born, contains no record of Willa Cather, but it does show that one of her younger brothers, Roscoe Boak Cather, was born on June 24, 1877, a date which makes December 7, 1876, obviously incorrect for Willa. I have not been able to find conclusive information; but what seems to be the best available evidence—three different entries in the records of the registrar of the University of Nebraska—indicates that although the day and month as usually given are correct, the year was neither 1876 nor 1875, but was, in fact, 1874. If so, Willa entered the state preparatory school at the somewhat more probable age of fifteen, was sixteen when she enrolled in the university itself the next year, and twenty when she graduated in June, 1895.

In any event, she had moved with her parents from Winchester, Virginia, to a farm near Red Cloud, Nebraska, in 1882. She spent only a few years in the public schools of Red Cloud, and was educated largely by her mother and her grandmothers, whose schooling of her in the Bible and in classical literature was a discipline which found lifelong reflection in the purity of Willa

Cather's written style. She acquired the rudiments of Greek and French from two local townspeople. With that background, she was sent to Lincoln, Nebraska, for the equivalent of a final year of high school training in the Latin School, which offered preparatory courses in connection with the state university.

A curious picture of the Willa Cather of that time has developed in recent years and is found repeatedly in biographical references to her. In it she appears, not as the precocious and intellectually sophisticated young woman she really was, but as a sort of wild girl of the West, riding across the prairies and listening openmouthed to the tales of the immigrant settlers. (Even her publishers have perpetuated the legend by stating on the jacket of one of her posthumous books that in Nebraska "Willa Cather spent most of her time riding about on her pony, visiting these foreign–born neighbors. . .") It is a harmless and romantic misconception which probably stems not so much from an identification of the author with the characters and settings of her stories, as from an attempt to fit Miss Cather into the setting of the Midwestern states, such as Nebraska, which many readers are still unable to think of as anything but wild, rough, and faintly comic.

It is true that Lincoln, Nebraska, was undoubtedly something less than the Athens of America, but for an alert and ambitious student it provided stimulating opportunities. Its university, which had been founded twenty years before, offered a solid, basically classical program of courses, sponsored student activities which were almost entirely intellectual, and included in its circle an amazing group of subsequently distinguished people.

The state university consisted of the Latin School, a two–year preparatory course; the Academic College, the one in which Miss Cather was enrolled; the Industrial College; the School of Fine Arts and Music; the College of Law; and the School of Graduate Instruction. In addition to the usual baccalaureate degrees, the Master of Arts and the Doctor of Philosophy degrees were offered. A typical four–year program in the Academic College, taking Willa Cather's program as an example, included eight full–year courses in English literature; three years of Greek; two years each of Latin and French; a year each of rhetoric, mathematics, and German; and one semester each of physical training, preparatory sciences, chemistry, American history, European history, philosophy, and journalism.

High scholastic standing was a prerequisite to any extra-curricular activity. There were baseball and football teams and a small program of intramural sports, in which Willa Cather's only part was an occasional vigorous but unskill-ful game of tennis. Aside from athletics, student activities of the time reflect the almost formidable seriousness of the whole school. Oratorical contests aroused as much excitement as a football game, if the space devoted to them in the student publications is an indication; and of a student body of about four hundred and fifty, it was not unusual for as many as two hundred enthusiastic supporters to accompany the school's debaters or orators to an out–of–town contest.

The centers of campus social life were the literary societies. Five of them had been founded by the time Willa

Cather joined the Union Literary Society. These organizations held frequent, regular meetings in clubrooms provided by the university, and conducted programs consisting of debates, dramatizations, orations, and music. Even though only incidentally so, the meetings were also social affairs. Young men escorted young ladies, and each society had an organized program for arranging partners for timorous members.

The Greek–letter social organizations came to the campus somewhat later than the literary societies, and although six of them had been chartered by 1890, their membership was still a minority of the students. Considered snobbish, the "Greeks" were a source of marked factionalism. Willa Cather never joined a Greek–letter sorority; she chose to write for and edit the *Hesperian,* a campus publication which represented the "anti–Greek" group. The university also sponsored a constantly fluctuating number of small clubs, organized to foster special interests such as writing, music, science, and religion.

Of two regularly issued student publications, the *Hesperian,* in which was published most of Willa Cather's first fiction and poetry, was a fortnightly magazine. The other was a monthly paper called the *Lasso,* which was replaced in 1894 by the *Nebraskan.* Generally speaking, the *Nebraskan* represented the fraternity group, the *Hesperian* the opposing faction. A senior yearbook or annual, the *Sombrero,* was first issued in 1892, and again in 1894, with Willa Cather as editor. The 1894 volume, dedicated to the Class of '95, has become a memorable one indeed, notable for several photographs of the cadet commandant,

Lieutenant John J. Pershing, and of Miss Cather; an article by Louise Pound; and a story written jointly by Dorothy Canfield and Willa Cather, possibly the most youthful collaboration by two famous literary figures ever published.

The *Hesperian,* of which Miss Cather was literary editor during her sophomore year, and managing editor during the year following, was a small magazine, usually of about sixteen pages. It contained some campus news, but was mainly literary in content, publishing stories, essays, poetry, and literary and dramatic news. Although it was written and edited by undergraduates, the quality of its writing was generally high, and noticeably at its peak during Willa Cather's editorship.

Miss Cather took part in student activities with an almost feverish energy. In addition to doing editorial work and writing for the *Hesperian* and the *Sombrero,* she served as critic and later as secretary of the Union Literary Society, appeared in at least three productions of the University Dramatic Club, was a member of a club formed for the study and admiration of the works of Lewis Carroll, traveled occasionally to Omaha and Chicago to see plays and operas, and during her senior year served as dramatic critic and columnist for a Lincoln daily newspaper.

In view of the schedule which all that activity must have meant, it is evidence of Miss Cather's mental energy that she passed all her courses in good standing, with the exception of one in mathematics. During her freshman year she failed to pass a required course in that subject and received a conditional standing, which was not removed until the month before her graduation. Many years later she told one of her sisters that the examination which she successfully passed for the removal of the conditional standing had become the source of a bad dream which persisted throughout her life, recurring whenever she was unusually fatigued. She would dream—just as it had actually occurred—that she sat outside her instructor's office, waiting for him to make his decision; in her dream, however, he always came out and told her that she had failed and could not graduate.

Even more than studies and activities, the phase of university life most likely to have influenced the young writer was the intense intellectual competition and stimulation of the people in the university and its circle. The school's chancellor was a distinguished and forceful educator, James H. Canfield, whose daughter Dorothea, later famous as Dorothy Canfield Fisher, was herself a student in the Latin School during part of the time when Willa Cather attended the university. On the faculty was Lieutenant John J. Pershing, professor of military science and tactics and Commandant of Cadets. Coming to the university from his first command with a detachment of Sioux Indian Scouts, this remarkable man not only conducted the Military Department, taught its courses, and served as an instructor in mathematics for two years, but also enrolled as a student and graduated from the College of Law in 1893. Other notable faculty members of that period were Charles E. Bessey, botanist, author, editor of scientific publications, and later president of the American Association for the Advancement of Science; and Lucius A. Sherman, noted as a critic, Shakespearean editor, and originator of a once–famous analytical method of literary criticism.

The comparatively small group of students included many who were later to achieve distinction—four as state governors, one as a United States Senator, two as members of Congress, and two as chancellors of state universities. Classmates of Miss Cather who would later distinguish themselves in scholarship included William L. Westermann, an authority on Greek and Egyptian history; Hartley B. Alexander, poet, philosopher and literary scholar; and Louise Pound, famous for research in folklore, balladry, linguistics, and literary history.

Also in Lincoln at the same time as Willa Cather were two men, both young lawyers, who though not directly connected with the university were associated with a group of its faculty and students. Willa Cather knew them both. One was Roscoe Pound, distinguished in the diverse fields of botany and law, who later served as professor of law at Nebraska, Northwestern, Chicago, and Harvard, and from 1916 to 1936 became the Harvard Law School's most memorable dean. The other young lawyer was William Jennings Bryan, who, in 1896, was to deliver the famous "Cross of Gold" oration at the Democratic national convention in Chicago, launching himself into national fame and three presidential nominations.

Willa Cather seems to have been peculiarly interested in Bryan, and she later wrote of him at some length. She had heard him deliver at least two speeches, including

"The Cross of Gold"; like most of his contemporaries, she was impressed by his oratory:

> Bryan came down to the sun–scorched, dried–up blown–away little village of Red Cloud to speak. . . There, with an audience of some few hundreds of bronzed farmers who believed in him as their deliverer, the man who could lead them out of the bondage of debt, who could stay the drought and strike water from the rock, I heard him make the greatest speech of his life. Surely that was eloquence of the old stamp that was called divine, eloquence that reached through the callous of ignorance and toil and found and awoke the stunted souls of men. I saw those rugged, ragged men of the soil weep like children. Six months later, at Chicago, when Bryan stampeded a convention, appropriated a party, electrified a nation, flashed his name around the planet, took the assembled thousands of that convention hall and molded them in his hands like so much putty, one of those ragged farmers sat beside me in the gallery, and at the close of that never–to–be–forgotten speech, he leaned over the rail, the tears on his furrowed cheeks, and shouted, "The sweet singer of Israel."

Even the fame of this man, however, could not repress the almost impertinent critical sense which was always characteristic of Willa Cather. For instance, she wrote:

> Living near him is like living near Niagara. The almighty, ever–renewed force of the man drives one to distraction, his everlasting high seriousness makes one want to play marbles.

She made many penetrating comments on Bryan, but probably none more significant than her comparison of him to the country from which he came:

So I think William Jennings Bryan synthetizes the entire middle West; all its newness and vigor, its magnitude and monotony, its richness and lack of variety, its inflammability and volubility, its strength and its crudeness, its high seriousness and self-confidence, its egotism and its nobility.

One other association of the time, brief but unquestionably impressive to her, was with the talented but neglected young writer, Stephen Crane. He had stopped in Lincoln while making his way, almost without money, from New York to Mexico. What she wrote later about her conversations with Crane is revealing, not only for what she tells of that unhappy genius, but also for what she says of herself at that time:

It was, I think, in the spring of '94, that a slender, narrow–chested fellow in a shabby grey suit, with a soft felt hat pulled low over his eyes, sauntered into the office of the managing editor of the *Nebraska State Journal* and introduced himself as Stephen Crane. . . I was doing some work for the *State Journal* in my leisure time, and I happened to be in the managing editor's room when Mr. Crane introduced himself. I was just off the range; I knew a little Greek and something about cattle and a good horse when I saw one, and beyond horses and cattle I considered nothing of vital importance except good stories and the people who wrote them . . This was the first man of letters I had ever met in the flesh, and when the young man announced who he was, I dropped into a chair behind the editor's desk where I could stare at him without being too much in evidence.

Stephen Crane was probably of special interest to her because she already had a close acquaintance with his work:

> "The Red Badge of Courage" had been published in the *State Journal* that winter along with a lot of other syndicate matter, and the grammatical construction of the story was so faulty that the managing editor had several times called on me to edit the copy. In this way I had read it very carefully, and through the careless sentence–structure I saw the wonder of that remarkable performance. But the grammar certainly was bad. I remember one of the reporters who had corrected the phrase "it don't" for the tenth time remarked savagely, "If I couldn't write better English than that, I'd quit."

Willa Cather's greater interest in literature than in her studies is shown by the tenacity with which she pursued Stephen Crane:

> I cut my classes to lie in wait for him, confident that in some unwary moment I could trap him into serious conversation, that if one burned incense long enough and ardently enough, the oracle would not be dumb. I was Maupassant mad at the time, a malady particularly unattractive in a Junior, and I made a frantic effort to get an expression of opinion from him on "Le Bonheur." "Oh, you're Moping, are you?" he remarked with a sarcastic grin, and went on reading a little volume of Poe that he carried in his pocket.

To her evident satisfaction, she succeeded in drawing from Crane a confirmation of her own disapproval of one of her instructor's methods of literary criticism:

23

We were taught literature by an exceedingly analytical method at the University, and we probably distorted the method, and I was busy trying to find the least common multiple of Hamlet and the greatest common divisor of Macbeth; and I began asking him whether stories were constructed by cabalistic formulas. At length he sighed wearily and shook his drooping shoulders, remarking: "Where did you get all that rot? Yarns aren't done by mathematics. You can't do it by rule anymore than you can dance by rule. You have to have the itch of the thing in your fingers, and if you haven't—well, you're damned lucky, and you'll live long and prosper, that's all."

During her last meeting with Crane, he talked long and bitterly of his views of life and of the writer's trade. Then, according to Miss Cather,

> . . . when the copy boy came in to take me home, I suggested to Crane that in ten years he would probably laugh at all his temporary discomfort. Again his body took on that strenuous tension and he clenched his hands, saying, "I can't wait ten years, I haven't time." The ten years are not up yet, and he has done his work and gathered his reward and gone.

Miss Cather worked for the *Journal* only occasionally during her last two years in college, and as far as the records of the paper reveal, without pay. However, she was attracting favorable attention. At about the time she graduated, another Lincoln newspaper, the *Courier,* included the following item in an editorial discussion of the quality of local newspapers:

> But on the whole the dramatic criticism is something to be proud of. Toby Rex of the *News* and Willa Cather of the *Journal* have done capital work, and

their writing is admired and enjoyed by intelligent and discriminating people.

Then, several weeks later the *Courier* announced:

> Miss Willa Cather, who for the past two years has been the dramatic critic and theatrical writer for the *Journal,* will become a member of the *Courier* staff. Miss Cather's reputation extends beyond Nebraska. She is thoroughly original and always entertaining. Her writing has a piquant literary flavor, and her services are a valuable acquisition to any paper.

Her work with the *Courier,* as an associate editor, until the end of November, 1895, was the last she did in Lincoln; she left soon for Pittsburgh, and the Nebraska years of Willa Cather had come to an end.

The articles, poems, dialogues, and stories collected in this volume will, if their author's youth is borne in mind, speak fairly for themselves. They are presented here, not with any pretension of literary greatness, but because they will be new to almost all of Willa Cather's readers, and because they will interest students of her art.

The collection includes, with very few exceptions, all the writing definitely identifiable as Willa Cather's which she produced while in Lincoln. The only intentional omissions are some of the newspaper articles and a story, the one already mentioned as being written in collaboration with Dorothy Canfield. It is omitted from this volume because of the joint authorship, but should be remembered by collectors of Willa Cather's early works. Under the title, "The Fear That Walks by Noonday," it tells, in an unintentionally amusing style, of a deceased football player whose ghost returns to win a game for his team.

All the writings included here were published with Miss Cather's name or initials, except for the newspaper writings from the *Journal*. The latter are identified by notations in the handwriting of Mr. Will O. Jones, the *Journal* editor, in one of his scrapbooks, now in the possession of the University of Nebraska library.

If any apology for the selection of the material in this volume is necessary, it probably should be for including the two short plays or dialogues. They are embarassingly juvenile, and it is difficult to believe that Miss Cather intended them seriously. They are presented only because they are curious examples of the experimentation so evident in her early writing. If the poems here reprinted seem a bit weighty with classical allusions, it should be recalled that they were written at a period when such pretentiousness was still conventional, and that they were written by a very young girl, whose youth makes all the more notable the remarkable smoothness of versification.

The stories show an artificiality which fortunately was not inherent in Miss Cather's style, a fact demonstrated by her much more vigorous and natural newspaper writing. However, these stories are significant, if for no other reason, because three of them—"Lou the Prophet," "Clemency of the Court," and "Peter"—are Midwestern in setting and highly suggestive of the themes and settings of *O Pioneers* and *My Ántonia*. They will probably come as a surprise to many who had assumed that in *O Pioneers* Miss Cather first used the pioneer Nebraska setting and the theme of the bewildered, struggling immigrant; actually that novel, published in 1913, was a return to these early stories, written some twenty years before.

Striking evidence of this connection is the unforgettable episode of the death of old Mr. Shimerda in *My Ántonia* which is almost directly taken from the story "Peter."

Writings from

Willa Cather's Campus Years

Dramatic Criticism and Comment

At the eleventh hour New York has awakened to the fact that Madame Melba is a great prima donna, so great indeed that there is none greater. She is a great singer rather than a great actress, and cannot equal Calve in her dramatic power. Nevertheless the wonderful lines of Gounod's "Juliet" were never sung better than she sings them. De Koven has said it.

Mr. Willard's Hamlet has fallen rather flat. A good many kindly suggestions are offered by his critics, but the principal trouble seems to be that Mr. Willard's Hamlet is not Hamlet at all. He plays the famous role without ranting or raving, but his quietness of manner, while it is impressive, is passive and unproductive. He makes a quiet, gentlemanly, practical, sensible Hamlet, and of course that spoils everything. Give Hamlet one grain of common sense and you have no play at all. Everything depends upon his being beautifully but unreasonably stupid. To put it more seriously, Mr. Willard tries to

31

interpret Hamlet's actions as influenced by the world outside, whereas Hamlet was a wholly subjective character and everything came from within.

February 11, 1894

It is with great joy that we learn that Julia Marlowe is going to play one of Sheridan Knowles' comedies instead of one of the immortal Shakespeare's. It is the greatest compliment that has been paid Lincoln intelligence for some time. Heretofore a great actor has seldom dared play anything but Shakespeare in Lincoln for the sake of his pocketbook. In all western provincial towns there is an idea that an actor can't be worth the price of admission when he plays neither blood curdling melodrama or Shakespeare. The same class of people whose favorite authors are Louisa M. Alcott and Browning go to the theatre only to see "Hamlet" or "In Old Kentucky." Of course the provincial audience complimented Shakespeare but the same people who applaud when Juliet takes the potion, fairly stand on their heads with delight when the spirited Queen Bess, whose last engagement was with a street car company, limps meekly out of the great conflagration scene. The great uneducated public have a sort of idea that Mr. Shakespeare was a great playright, and as he is the only playwright they know anything about they admire him very much. Now the fact is there have been several other playwrights, and it is time Lincoln found it out. It is rather promising if an actress dares to appear here in any other role than Rosalind or Viola.

February 25, 1894

Julia Marlowe has come and gone again, leaving with us a sort of warm, rich delight that will hover about us for days. There is about her a quaint and subtle fascination like that of the rare old comedies she plays. There seems to be no adjective or adverb or combination of the two that can at all describe Julia Marlowe, anyone who seriously set out to find them would be driven crazy in a week. It is the beauty that glimpses from certain old pictures and lines from certain old pastorals have. We are not often subjected to the influence of beauty pure and simple, beauty of face, beauty of acting, beauty of form and movement, and when we are it has a peculiar effect on us. Miss Marlowe is the embodiment of beauty and good taste and good spirits, and she is very little more. Her acting is just one constant exhibition of fine taste— taste for the quaint and poetic in literature, for fine detail and richness in scenery, for color and beauty in costumes. The scenery which made the Lansing stage so artistically beautiful we hardly knew it is only an example of that quality which governs her art. Miss Marlowe is honest and conscientious enough in her own work, but she has not a particle of heart. In all that discomfort and pique of hers in the fourth act there was never a particle of real pain. At the end, where any other woman would have given Wildrake and the audience satisfaction by a little judicious and discreet affection, Miss Marlowe proposes a dance to exhibit her grace and her costume. I remember every attitude she struck in "Twelfth Night," but I do not remember any acting which gave anything of the undercurrent of passion in the play. One can never forget the sweet womanly delight that steals over Modjeska's Rosalind when she reads those poems hung about in the forest, and that great fainting of hers at the sight of Orlando's blood. Miss Marlowe is only amused when she reads those sonnets, and one cannot for the life of him recall how she fainted or whether she fainted at all, though he can remember every crinkle in those delicious russet boots of hers. When one looks into that beautiful face that expresses all light emotions so wonderfully, one knows that great passions could never struggle in it. Miss Marlowe never can escape from her own prettiness—made actresses have not such a temptation thrown in their way. She could never hollow her cheeks as Camille nor scar her flesh in "Article 47," and I don't think anyone is anxious to see her do it. She cannot rise above the sense of her own beauty, and when we see her dancing as she did the other night we do not wish her to do it. Modjeska frequently forgets herself and goes on the stage with her costume all awry. Bernhardt sometimes dashes on the stage leaving half of it off altogether. Miss Marlowe would never be guilty of such carelessness. On the stage she lives too beautifully to live very hard, dies too gracefully to die very effectively. This is all very winning and beautiful, but it is not the highest kind of art. Mr. Whistler's nocturnes in color are ravishingly beautiful things, but they have not the power or the greatness of the old faded frescoes that told roughly of hell and heaven and death and judgment. After all the supreme virtue in all art is soul, perhaps it is the only thing which gives art a right to be. The greatest art in acting is not to please and charm and delight, but to move and thrill; not to play a part daintily or delightfully, but with power and passion. All prettiness for its own sake is trivial, all beauty for beauty's sake is sensual. No matter how dainty, how refined, how spirituelle, it is still a thing of the senses only.

March 4, 1894

The dramatic papers and newspapers and papers generally are concerning themselves wonderfully over Booth's successor. There is even a good deal of feeling as to whether he will be Mr. Whitesides or Mr. Willard. The public seem to think they have only to name Booth's successor to cause him to appear, that if they only give an actor permission he will straightway go and be Booth. Now the truth is the public needn't trouble themselves for it won't do any good. If, after Shakespeare's death, the learned English doctors had got together and elected another Shakespeare, much use it would have been. We can elect Benjamin Harrison's and Grover Cleveland's any day, but Booth's and Shakespeare's have to be balloted on in heaven. We will just have to patiently wait until God and nature are pleased to give us another Booth, and it may be a long old wait, for we can't hurry the tide of destiny.

March 4, 1894

. . . Bernhardt's really great acting is limited to the expression of just one passion, and that passion she can represent in every phase of pain and delight, desire and fulfillment, rapture and anguish, in every phase except the more spiritual phases. All her heroic and disinterested passions are clever imitations, there is only one that is genuine with her, only one that she greatly feels herself or can make others feel greatly. No other actress has ever lived who could love on the stage like Bernhardt. It is so genuine that part of the time it seemed wicked to look at her and part of the time rude. She is the only actress I ever saw who seemed to desperately enjoy stage caresses, and does them genuinely and not at all in the conventional way, and with very evident purpose, until she seems to perfectly lose her head over them and forgets to go on with the play. What other actresses take for granted she revels in, and she makes it impressive, too. She is never sentimental, it is all too sudden, too unrestrained, too violent for that. Her bursts of passion blind one by their vividness. Afterward you cannot remember how she looked or what she did. It is like lightning gone before you see enough of it, and indescribable in its brilliancy.

March 4, 1894

The Chicago papers are raving over Modjeska in "Mary Stuart." "Regal, queenly, womanly" are a few of the glowing adjectives applied to her. Of course, no adjectives can be too strong for Modjeska, but one wonders how she really plays the role, whether she is the grand, stately, regal queen of Schiller, or the vain, impulsive, sentimental queen of history. Of course, Schiller idealized Mary Stuart, the Germans have such an awful habit of idealizing their women. Schiller has almost made the world forget that Mary was Gallic by choice and education, that she wept all day on leaving France, that it was France that was supposed to be graven on her heart. In prison it was not Scotland but France she sighed for. The hatred between Mary and Elizabeth was no mere personal hatred, it was the incompatibility of two races. The trouble with Mary was that she tried to establish a Tuilleries in solemn, bag-pipe, Presbyterian Scotland. She is always played and written of as though she were a sort of national saint, whereas in truth there were Italian tenors and supper episodes and divers marriages, just as there are nowadays.

March 11, 1894

All year we have been opposed by a vague, indescribable dread. Every time we have seen the bill posters putting up posters we have shuddered lest we should see her name, or, more still, her picture. It has been a hard year, theatrically and otherwise, and we have had most of the seven plagues of Egypt poured upon us, but we have hoped the Lord would spare us Maggie [Mitchell], and it almost seems that he is going to. We have seen her pictures yearly ever since we were little, and we have grown unspeakably weary of them and of her. Fifty years ago, when Maggie was young she had nothing but a laugh with mirth in it and a face with a moderate allowance of beauty. But how any actress can be so behind as to imagine that she is beautiful after she is seventy remains unexplained. If she played parts like Mrs. Drew, her age would be gladly pardoned and forgotten. But to see a woman of seventy, old and shrunken and "wrinkled deep in time," painted and padded and schottishing about the stage is more than most of us can stand with comfort. The year is so far advanced now, that we almost begin to breathe freely. Perhaps she may not come after all. Yet such good fortune must portend something very dark. If she really spares us this time, we had better have overskirts and big sleeves put on our ascension robes, we will need them this year.

March 11, 1894

. . . The day is long since past when an actor is classed with a circus rider. Today a great actor is recognized as a gentleman and an artist. An actor is no longer looked upon as an imitator, but is an author who writes a book every night, an artist who every evening paints a picture in the gas light. The day will come when the profession will attain still higher honor. An actor's life is the hardest of all the hard lives men lead for art's value. Other men can do their work and forget the travail in success. But an actor's creation must be born again every night out of his own brain sweat. He should have all working while he lives for when he dies his work dies with him. Poets can die trusting their work to the appreciation of the future, but an actor's greatness dies in him, as music dies in a broken lute.

April 8, 1894

The most finished performance that Lincoln has seen for a long time or will see for a long time to come was that of Richard Mansfield at the Lansing theatre last Monday night. The whole play was like a chapter from Henry Esmond, in some way it was entirely Thackeray-esque. It was saturated with the spirit of the time and people that Thackeray loved to deal with. Mr. Mansfield is perfectly self–contained and self–sufficient. He depends very little upon the applause or appreciation of his audience, and on this one occasion it was very fortunate for him that it was so. He has intellectual standards that are unshaken by the chance emotions of the hour. He seldom so much as glances across the footlights, he is unconscious that the gallery exists. More than any other actor he acts for the play and for himself. His acting is conscientious because he is unconscious of anything but his part. It is easy to believe that Mr. Mansfield was a painter for ten years of his life. He has the artistic love of modulated color and sound. He carries the sense of tone and tone color even into his acting. His Beau Brummel is perfectly even in pitch. Of course the quality of intensity changes in different situations, but the quantity does not vary. The pain of exquisite perfection of the first act and the sub-dued boredness on his face in the dance were as genuinely painful as the havoc of suffering and starvation that stamped his countenance in the last two acts. In the first part of the play his prosperity was toned down by his utter correctness, in the last part his poverty was elevated by the man's innate refinement. The whole creation of Beau Brummell is like a picture in which everything must echo and savor of the predominating color. It is easy to see that Mr. Mansfield is an intelligent and educated man. Any actor with an emotional nature can play roles in which the emotions are simple and decided. He had only to work himself up and let himself loose. Thomas Keene, by limping and leering and hissing, manages to make the public believe he can play "Richard III," because the popular conception of Richard is only that he should be as wicked and disagreeable as possible. Robert Downing deludes people into thinking he can play "Virginus" because he is fat and oratorical. Hate, love, nobleness in the theory and the abstract are easy things to enact. But the emotions in the role of Beau Brummell are delicate, complex, negative, almost contradictory. It requires as much intelligence and insight as Hamlet. Most very good actors would be vulgar fops in the part; it requires a scholar and a gentleman to portray it, it takes culture of mind and delicacy of instinct to comprehend it. There is but one living novelist who could handle the character in a novel, George Meredith; but one living actor who can act it, Richard Mansfield. The two men suggest each other in many ways, though perhaps it is only because they are two of the very few serenely great in this troubled, feverish century.   April 15, 1894

It is too bad that romantic ideals can never last in this world. The most un–matter of fact personage on the stage has been Elenora Duse. She was so white and distant and delicate that she hardly seemed a thing of clay, but someone apart engrossed wholly by art and consumption. The latest dispatches from Rome say that she stopped there on her way to Naples, and that she is fat and florid and has begun to lace and has to make up for her death scene in "Camille." German cabbages evidently agreed with the signora. April 15, 1894

The twenty-third of April has come and gone again, just as it has done for three hundred and thirty years since it was made hallowed to the world. I wonder how many people know or care that it has come again. Perhaps some few Shakespearean scholars who are scholars rejoiced that morning, and a great many professional people and perhaps the stars that mete out human fate, and the angels, if there are any. But the people of the world, who call themselves society, and the people of the schools, who call themselves culture, knew little and cared less. We have a Thanksgiving day in memory of blessings we never get, a Fourth of July in memory of a document that is largely a dead letter, a George Washington's day, a Saint Patrick's day in memory of nonsense and an Arbor Day in memory of nothing whatever, but the day of William Shakespeare's birth passes without honor or recognition, except among the faithful hearts of a despised population. Even the light opera and comedy people know and reverence that day which pastors and professors do not recognize. Julia Marlowe, with that womanly sweetness and delicacy characteristic of her, spent the day and night in solitude, in contemplation and adoration of Mary Arden, who, as a Chicago critic beautifully puts it, is almost as much to be envied among women as that other Mary of holy memory.

April 15, 1894

Fiction

PETER

"No, Antone, I have told thee many, many times, no, thou shalt not sell it until I am gone."

"But I need money; what good is that old fiddle to thee? The very crows laugh at thee when thou art trying to play. Thy hand trembles so thou canst scarce hold the bow. Thou shalt go with me to the Blue to cut wood tomorrow. See to it thou art up early."

"What, on the Sabbath, Antone, when it is so cold? I get so very cold, my son, let us not go tomorrow."

"Yes, tomorrow, thou lazy old man. Do not cut wood upon the Sabbath? Care I how cold it is? Wood thou shalt cut, and haul it too, and as for the fiddle, I tell thee I will sell it yet." Antone pulled his ragged cap down over his low, heavy brow, and went out. The old man drew his stool up nearer the fire, and sat stroking his violin with trembling fingers and muttering, "Not while I live, not while I live."

Five years ago they had come here, Peter Sadelack, and his wife, and oldest son Antone, and countless smaller Sadelacks, here to southwestern Nebraska, and had taken up a homestead. Antone was the acknowledged master of the premises, and people said he was a likely youth, and would do well. That he was mean and untrustworthy every one knew, but that made little difference. His corn was better tended than any in the county, and his wheat always yielded more than other men's.

Of Peter no one knew much, nor had any one a good word to say for him. He drank whenever he could get out of Antone's sight long enough to pawn his hat or coat for whiskey. Indeed there were but two things he would not pawn, his pipe and his violin. He was a lazy, absent minded old fellow, who liked to fiddle better than to plow, though Antone surely got work enough out of them all, for that matter. In the house of which Antone was master there was no one, from the little boy three years old, to the old man of sixty, who did not earn his bread. Still people said that Peter was worthless, and was a great drag on Antone, his son, who never drank, and was a much better man than his father had ever been. Peter did not care what people said. He did not like the country, nor the people, least of all he liked the plowing. He was very homesick for Bohemia. Long ago, only eight years ago by the calendar, but it seemed eight centuries to Peter, he had been a second violinist in the great theatre at Prague. He had gone into the theatre very young, and had been there all his life, until he had a stroke of paralysis, which made his arms so weak that his bowing was uncertain. Then they told him he could go. Those were great days at the theatre. He had plenty to drink then, and wore a dress coat every evening, and there were always parties after the play. He could play in those days, ay, that he could! He could never read the notes well, so he did not play first; but his touch, he had a touch indeed, so Herr Mikilsdoff, who led the orchestra, had said. Sometimes now Peter thought he could plow better if he could only bow as he used to. He had seen all the lovely women in the world there, all the great singers and the great players. He was in the orchestra when Rachel played, and he heard Liszt play when the Countess d'Agoult sat in the stage box and threw the master white lilies. Once, a French woman came and played for weeks, he did not remember her name now. He did not remember her face very well either, for it changed so, it was never twice the same. But the beauty of it, and the great hunger men felt at the sight of it, that he remembered. Most of all he remembered her voice. He did not know French, and could not understand a word she said, but it seemed to him that she must be talking the music of Chopin. And her voice, he thought he should know that in the other world. The last night she played a play in which a man touched her arm and she stabbed him. As Peter sat among the smoking gas jets down below the footlights with his fiddle on his knee, and looked up to her, he thought he would like to die, too, if he could touch her arm once, and have her stab him so. Peter went home to his wife very drunk that night. Even in those days he was a foolish fellow, who cared for nothing but music and pretty faces.

It was all different now. He had nothing to drink and little to eat, and here, there was nothing but sun, and grass, and sky. He had forgotten almost everything, but some things he remembered well enough. He loved his violin and the holy Mary, and above all else he feared the Evil One, and his son Antone.

The fire was low, and it grew cold. Still Peter sat by the fire remembering. He dared not throw more cobs on the fire; Antone would be angry. He did not want to cut wood tomorrow, it would be Sunday, and he wanted to go to mass. Antone might let him do that. He held his violin under his wrinkled chin, his white hair fell over it, and he began to play "Ave Maria." His hand shook more than ever before, and at last refused to work the bow at all. He sat stupefied for awhile, then rose, and taking his violin with him, stole out into the old stable. He took Antone's shot-gun down from its peg, and loaded it by the moonlight which streamed in through the door. He sat down on the dirt floor, and leaned back against the dirt wall. He heard the wolves howling in the distance, and the night wind screaming as it swept over the snow. Near him he heard the regular breathing of the horses in the dark. He put his crucifix above his heart, and folding his hands said brokenly all the Latin he had ever known, "Pater noster, qui in coelum est." Then he raised his head and sighed, "Not one kreutzer will Antone pay them to pray for my soul, not one kreutzer, he is so careful of his money, is Antone; he does not waste it in drink, he is a better man than I, but hard sometimes; he works the girls too hard; women were not made to work so; but he shall not sell thee, my fiddle, I can play thee not more, but they shall not part us; we have seen it all together, and we will forget it together, the French woman and all." He held his fiddle under his chin a moment, where it had lain so often, then put it across his knee and broke it through the middle. He pulled off his old boot, held the gun between his knees with the muzzle against his forehead, and pressed the trigger with his toe.

In the morning Antone found him stiff, frozen fast in a pool of blood. They could not straighten him out enough to fit a coffin, so they buried him in a pine box. Before the funeral Antone carried to town the fiddlebow which Peter had forgotten to break. Antone was very thrifty, and a better man than his father had been.

Hesperian, XXII:4, Nov. 24, 1892, pp. 10–12

LOU, THE PROPHET

It had been a very trying summer to every one, and most of all to Lou. He had been in the West for seven years, but he had never quite gotten over his homesickness for Denmark. Among the northern people who emigrate to the great west, only the children and the old people ever long much for the lands they have left over the water. The men only know that in this new land their plow runs across the field tearing up the fresh, warm earth, with never a stone to stay its course. That if they dig and delve the land long enough, and if they are not compelled to mortgage it to keep body and soul together, some day it will be theirs, their very own. They are not like the southern people; they loose their love for their fatherland quicker and have less of sentiment about them. They have to think too much about how they shall get bread to care much what soil gives it to them. But among even the most blunted, mechanical people, the youths and the aged always have a touch of romance in them.

Lou was only twenty-two; he had been but a boy when his family left Denmark, and had never ceased to remember it. He was a rather simple fellow, and was always considered less promising than his brothers; but last year he had taken up a claim of his own and made a rough dug-out upon it and he lived there all alone. His life was that of many another young man in our country. He rose early in the morning, in the summer just before day-break; in the winter, long before. First he fed his stock, then himself, which was a much less important matter. He ate the same food at dinner that he ate at breakfast, and the same at supper that he ate at dinner. His bill of fare never changed the year round; bread, coffee, beans and sorghum molasses, sometimes a little salt pork. After breakfast he worked until dinner time, ate, and then worked again. He always went to bed soon after the sun set, for he was always tired, and it saved oil. Sometimes, on Sundays, he would go over home after he had done his washing and house cleaning, and sometimes he hunted. His life was as sane and as uneventful as the life of his plow horses, and it was as hard and thankless. He was thrifty for a simple, thick-headed fellow, and in the spring he was to have married Nelse Sorenson's daughter, but he had lost all his cattle during the winter, and was not so prosperous as he had hoped to be; so, instead she married her cousin, who had an "eighty" of his own. That hurt Lou more than anyone ever dreamed.

A few weeks later his mother died. He had always loved his mother. She had been kind to him and used to come over to see him sometimes, and shake up his hard bed for him, and sweep, and make his bread. She had a strong affection for the boy, he was her youngest, and she always felt sorry for him; she had danced a great

47

deal before his birth, and an old woman in Denmark had told her that was the cause of the boy's weak head.

Perhaps the greatest calamity of all was the threatened loss of his corn crop. He had bought a new corn planter on time that spring, and had intended that his corn should pay for it. Now, it looked as though he would not have corn enough to feed his horses. Unless rain fell within the next two weeks, his entire crop would be ruined; it was half gone now. All these things together were too much for poor Lou, and one morning he felt a strange loathing for the bread and sorghum which he usually ate as mechanically as he slept. He kept thinking about the strawberries he used to gather on the mountains after the snows were gone, and the cold water in the mountain streams. He felt hot someway, and wanted cold water. He had no well, and he hauled his water from a neighbor's well every Sunday, and it got warm in the barrels those hot summer days. He worked at his haying all day; at night, when he was through feeding, he stood a long time by the pig stye with a basket on his arm. When the moon came up, he sighed restlessly and tore the buffalo pea flowers with his bare toes. After a while, he put his basket away, and went into his hot, close, little dug-out. He did not sleep well, and he dreamed a horrible dream. He thought he saw the Devil and all his angels in the air holding back the rain clouds, and they loosed all the damned in Hell, and they came, poor tortured things, and drank up whole clouds of rain. Then he thought a strange light shown from the south, just over the river bluffs, and the clouds parted, and Christ and all his angels were descending. They were coming, coming, myriads and myriads of them, in a great blaze of glory. Then he felt something give way in his poor, weak head, and with a cry of pain he awoke. He lay shuddering a long time in the dark, then got up and lit his lantern and took from the shelf his mother's bible. It opened of itself at Revelations, and Lou began to read, slowly indeed, for it was hard work for him. Page by page, he read those burning, blinding, blasting words, and they seemed to shrivel up his poor brain altogether. At last the book slipped from his hands and he sank down upon his knees in prayer, and stayed so until the dull gray dawn stole over the land and he heard the pigs clamoring for their feed.

He worked about the place until noon, and then prayed and read again. So he went on several days, praying and reading and fasting, until he grew thin and haggard. Nature did not comfort him any, he knew nothing about nature, he had never seen her; he had only stared into a black plow furrow all his life. Before, he had only seen in the wide, green lands and the open blue the possibilities of earning his bread; now, he only saw in them a great world ready for the judgment, a funeral pyre ready for the torch.

One morning, he went over to the big prairie dog town, where several little Danish boys herded their fathers' cattle. The boys were very fond of Lou; he never teased them as the other men did, but used to help them with their cattle, and let them come over to his dug-out to make sorghum taffy. When they saw him coming, they ran to meet him and asked him where he had been all these days. He did not answer their questions, but said: "Come into the cave, I want to see you."

Some six or eight boys herded near the dog town every summer, and by their combined efforts they had dug a cave in the side of a high bank. It was large enough to hold them all comfortably, and high enough to stand in.

There the boys used to go when it rained or when it was cold in the fall. They followed Lou silently and sat down on the floor. Lou stood up and looked tenderly down into the little faces before him. They were old-faced little fellows, though they were not over twelve or thirteen years old; hard work matures boys quickly.

"Boys," he said earnestly, "I have found out why it don't rain, it's because of the sins of the world. You don't know how wicked the world is, it's all bad, all, even Denmark. People have been sinning a long time, but they won't much longer. God has been watching and watching for thousands of years, and filling up the phials of wrath, and now he is going to pour out his vengeance and let Hell loose upon the world. He is burning up our corn now, and worse things will happen; for the sun shall be as sack-cloth, and the moon shall be like blood, and the stars of heaven shall fall, and the heavens shall part like a scroll, and the mountains shall be moved out of their places, and the great day of his wrath shall come, against which none may stand. Oh, boys! the floods and the flames shall come down upon us together and the whole world shall perish." Lou paused for breath, and the little boys gazed at him in wonder. The sweat was running down his haggard face, and his eyes were staring wildly. Presently, he resumed in a softer tone, "Boys, if you want rain, there is only one way to get it, by prayer. The people of the world won't pray, perhaps if they did God would not hear them, for they are so wicked; but he will hear you, for you are little children and are likened unto the kingdom of heaven, and he loved ye."

Lou's haggard, unshaven face bent toward them and his blue eyes gazed at them with terrible earnestness.

"Show us how, Lou," said one little fellow in an awed whisper. Lou knelt down in the cave, his long, shaggy hair hung down over his face, and his voice trembled as he spoke:

"Oh God, they call thee many long names in thy book, thy prophets; but we are only simple folk, the boys are all little and I am weak headed ever since I was born, therefore, let us call thee Father, for thy other names are hard to remember. O Father, we are so thirsty, all the world is thirsty; the creeks are all dried up, and the river is so low that the fishes die and rot in it; the corn is almost gone; the hay is light; and even the little flowers are no more beautiful. O God! our corn may yet be saved. O, give us rain! Our corn means so much to us, if it fails, all our pigs and cattle will die, and we ourselves come very near it; but if you do not send rain, O Father, and if the end is indeed come, be merciful to thy great, wicked world. They do many wrong things, but I think they forget thy word, for it is a long book to remember, and some are little, and some are born weak headed, like me, and some are born very strong headed, which is near as bad. Oh, forgive them their abominations in all the world, both in Denmark and here, for the fire hurts so, O God! Amen."

The little boys knelt and each said a few blundering words. Outside, the sun shone brightly and the cattle nibbled at the short, dry grass, and the hot wind blew through the shriveled corn; within the cave, they knelt as many another had knelt before them, some in temples, some in prison cells, some in the caves of earth, and One, indeed, in the garden, praying for the sin of the world.

The next day, Lou went to town, and prayed in the streets. When the people saw his emaciated frame and wild eyes, and heard his wild words, they told the sheriff to do his duty, the man must be mad. Then Lou ran away; he ran for miles, then walked and limped and stumbled on, until he reached the cave; there the boys found him in the morning. The officials hunted him for days, but he hid in the cave, and the little Danes kept his secret well. They shared their dinners with him, and prayed with him all day long. They had always liked him, but now they would have gone straight through fire for him, any one of them, they almost worshipped him. He had about him that mysticism which always appeals so quickly to children. I have always thought that bear story which the Hebrews used to tell their children very improbable. If it was true, then I have my doubts about the prophet; no one in the world will hoot at insincere and affected piety sooner than a child, but no one feels the true prophetic flame quicker, no one is more readily touched by simple goodness. A very young child can tell a sincere man better than any phrenologist.

One morning, he told the boys that he had had another "true dream." He was not going to die like other men, but God was going to take him to himself as he was. The end of the world was close at hand, too very close. He prayed more than usual that day, and when they sat eating their dinner in the sunshine, he suddenly sprang to his feet and stared wildly south, crying, "See, see, it is the great light! the end comes!! and they do not know it; they will keep on sinning, I must tell them, I must!"

"No, no, Lou, they will catch you; they are looking for you, you must not go!"

"I must go, my boys; but first let me speak once more to you. Men would not heed me, or believe me, because my head is weak, but you have always believed in me, that God has revealed his word to me, and I will pray God to take you to himself quickly, for ye are worthy. Watch and pray always, boys, watch the light over the bluffs, it is breaking, breaking, and shall grow brighter.

Good bye, my boys, I must leave ye in the world yet awhile." He kissed them all tenderly and blessed them, and started south. He walked at first, then he ran, faster and faster he went, all the while shouting at the top of his voice, "The sword of the Lord and of Gideon!"

The police officers heard of it, and set out to find him. They hunted the country over and even dragged the river, but they never found him again, living or dead. It is thought that he was drowned and the quicksands of the river sucked his body under. But the little Dane boys in our country firmly believe that he was translated like Enoch of old. On stormy nights, when the great winds sweep down from the north they huddle together in their beds and fancy that in the wind they still hear that wild cry, "The sword of the Lord and of Gideon."

*Hesperian,*XXII:1, Oct. 15, 1892, pp. 7–10

A TALE OF THE WHITE PYRAMID

(I, Kakau, son of Ramenka, high priest of Phtahah in the great temple at Memphis, write this, which is an account of what I, Kakau, saw on the first day of my arrival at Memphis, and the first day of my sojourn in the home of Rui, my uncle, who was a priest of Phtahah before me.)

As I drew near the city the sun hung hot over the valley which wound like a green thread toward the south. On either side the river lay the fields of grain, and beyond was the desert of yellow sand which stretched away to where the low line of Lybian hills rose against the sky. The heat was very great, and the breeze scarce stirred the reeds which grew in the black mud down where the Nile, like a great tawny serpent, crept lazily away through the desert. Memphis stood as silent as the judgment hall of Osiris. The shops and even the temples were deserted, and no man stirred in the streets save the watchmen of the city. Early in the morning the people had arisen and washed the ashes from their faces, shaved their bodies, taken off the robes of mourning, and had gone out into the plain, for the seventy-two days of mourning were now over.

Senefrau the first, Lord of the Light and Ruler of the Upper and Lower Kingdoms, was dead and gathered unto his fathers. His body had passed into the hands of the embalmers, and lain for the allotted seventy days in niter, and had been wrapped in gums and spices and white linen and placed in a golden mummy case, and to-day it was to be placed in the stone sarcophagus in the white pyramid, where it was to await its soul.

Early in the morning, when I came unto the house of my uncle, he took me in his chariot and drove out of the city into the great plain which is north of the city, where the pyramid stood. The great plain was covered with a multitude of men. There all the men of the city were gathered together, and men from all over the land of Khem. Here and there were tethered many horses and camels of those who had come from afar. The army was there, and the priesthood, and men of all ranks; slaves, and swineherds, and the princes of the people. At the head of the army stood a tall dark man in a chariot of ivory and gold, speaking with a youth who stood beside the chariot.

"It is Kufu, the king," said Rui, "men say that before the Nile rises again he will begin to build a pyramid, and that it will be such a one as men have never seen before, nor shall we afterwards."

"Who is he that stands near unto the king, and with whom the king speaks?" I asked. Then there came a cloud upon the face of Rui, the brother of my father, and he answered and said unto me:

"He is a youth of the Shepherd people of the north, he is a builder and has worked upon the tomb. He is cunning of hand and wise of heart, and Kufu has shown him

55

great favor, but the people like him not, for he is of the blood of strangers."

I spoke no more of the youth, for I saw that Rui liked him not, but my eyes were upon him continually, for I had seen no other man like unto him for beauty of face or of form.

After a time it came to pass that the great tumult ceased throughout the plain, and the words of men died upon their lips. Up from the shore of the sacred lake wound the funeral procession toward the tomb, and by the Lord of Truth I then thought the glory of Isis could be no grander. There were boys clad in white and wreathed with lotus flowers, and thousands of slaves clad in the skins of leopards, bearing bread and wine and oil, and carrying the images of the gods. There were maidens, bands of harpers and of musicians, and the captives which the king had taken in war leading tigers and lions of the desert. There was the sacred ark drawn by twenty white oxen, and there were many priests, and the guards of the king, and the sacred body of Senefrau, borne by carriers. After the body of the king came all the women of his household, beating their hearts, and weeping bitterly. As the train approached men fell upon their faces and prayed to Pthahah, the Great South Wall, and Kufu bowed his head. At the foot of the pyramid the train halted, and the youths clothed in white, and the priests, and those who bore the body began to ascend the pyramid, singing as they went:

Enter into thy rest, oh Pharaoh!
Enter into thy kingdom.
For the crown of the two lands was heavy,
And thy head was old,
And thou hast laid it aside forever.
Thy two arms were weak,

And the scepter was a great weight,
And thou hast put it from thee.
Enter thou into thy new reign,
Longer than the eternities.
Darkness shall be thy realm, O king,
And sleep thy minion.
The chariots of Ethiopia shall surround thee no more,
Nor the multitudes of the mighty encompass thee in battle,
For thou, being dead, art become as a god;
Good thou knowest, oh king;
And evil has been nigh unto thee,
Yet neither approach thee now,
For thou art dead, and like unto the gods.

They bore him down into the pyramid, and left him to sleep, and to wait. Then I saw a multitude of men gather about a great white stone that lay at the base of the tomb, and I questioned Rui concerning it, and he answered me:

"This pyramid as thou seest opens not at the side, but from the top down. That great slab of stone is to cover the top of the tomb. See, even now the workmen spread mortar upon the top of the tomb, and fasten ropes about the great stone to lift it into place. Neith grant that they harm not the stone, for it has taken a thousand men ten years to cut and polish it and to bring it thither."

I saw slaves bending over the great stone, fastening about it ropes which hung from the great pulleys built upon the shafts which rose from the upper stage of the pyramid. While they did this, companies of slaves began to ascend the sides of the tomb, each company with its master. The men were all fashioned like the men of the north, and their strength was like ribbed steel, for these were the mightiest men in Egypt. After a time there was silence in the plain. The slaves took hold of the ropes that swung from the pulleys, and every voice was hushed. It was as still without the pryamid as it was within. At last the sound of the Sistrum broke the stillness, the master builders waved their lashes, and the two thousand slaves who were upon the pyramid set their feet firmly upon the polished stone and threw the weight of their bodies upon the ropes. Slowly, slowly, amid the creaking and groaning of the ropes, the great stone left the earth. The musicians played and the people shouted, for never before in all Egypt had so great a stone been raised. But suddenly the shouting ceased, and the music was hushed, and a stillness like the sleep of Nut fell over the plain. All the people gazed upward, and the heart of Khem grew sick as they looked. The great stone had risen half way, the lifting ropes were firm as the pillars of heaven, but one of the ropes which held the stone in place gave way and stretched, and the great stone which was the pride of the land, was settling at one end and slipping from its fastenings. The slaves crouched upon the pyramid, the builders spoke no word, and the people turned their eyes from the stone, that they might not see it fall. As I looked up, I saw a man running rapidly along the tier of the pyramid opposite the rocking stone. I knew his face to be the face of the stranger whom I saw speaking with the king. He threw off his garments as he ran, and at the edge of the stone tier he paused for a moment, he crouched low, gathering all his strength, then suddenly straightening his body he threw back his head and shot straight forward, like an arrow shot from the bow, over eighteen cubits, and fell lightly upon his feet on the uppermost end of the stone. He stood with both hands clenched at his side, his right foot a little before his left, erect and fair as the statue of Houris, watching the farther end of

58

the stone. For a little the stone stood still, then swung back and lay evenly as when all was well, and then the end upon which the youth stood, sank. He thrust his right foot further forward, his toes clinging to the polished stone, and clasping his hands about his waist above the hips, slowly bowed his great frame forward. The stone slab felt its master and swung slowly back, and again the end on which the youth stood was uppermost. So he stood, his dusky limbs showing clear against the white stone, his every muscle quivering, the sweat pouring from his body, swaying the great stone. The great white desert seemed to rock and sway, the sun grew hotter and stood still in heaven, the sky and the sea of faces seemed to whirl and reel, then blend into one awful face, grinning horribly. The slaves, not daring to breathe, crouched upon the tomb, the multitude stood still and gazed upward, and earth and heaven and men were as dumb as if the gods had smitten them mad with thunder. Then a great cry rang out:

"In the name of Phtahah and of your fathers' souls, pull!"

It was the voice of Kufu. Slowly, like men awakened from a dream, the slaves drew up that swinging stone, and he stood upon it. Below the king stood, his hands clutching the front of his chariot, and his eyes strained upon the stone. When the slab reached the top of the shaft on which the pulley hung, it was swung back over the pyramid, and the descent began. The slaves, sick with fear, lost control of it, and the great stone plunged down faster and faster. I wondered if the mortar spread upon the top was thick enough to break its fall. Just as it struck the top in safety, he who stood upon it, gathering all his strength leaped high into the air to break the shock and fell motionless upon the stone. Then such a cry as went up, never before roused old Nilus from his dreams, or made the walls of the city to tremble. They bore him down from the tomb and placed him in the chariot of the king. Then the king's trumpeter sounded, and then Kufu spake:

"We have this day seen a deed the like of which we have never seen before, neither have our fathers told us of such a thing. Know, men of Egypt that he, the Shepherd stranger, who has risen upon the swinging stone, shall build the great pyramid, for he is worthy in my sight. The king has said."

Then the people cheered, but their faces were dark. And the charioteer of the king lashed his horses across the plain toward the city.

Of the great pyramid and of the mystery thereof, and of the strange builder, and of the sin of the king, I may not speak, for my lips are sealed.

Hesperian, XXII:5, Dec. 22, 1892, pp. 8–11

A SON OF THE CELESTIAL

A CHARACTER

Ah lie me dead in the sunrise land,
Where the sky is blue and the hills are gray,
Where the camels doze in the desert sun,
And the sea gulls scream o'er the big blue bay.

Where the Hwang–Ho glides through the golden sand,
And the herons play in the rushes tall,
Where pagodas rise upon every hill
And the peach trees bloom by the Chinese wall.

Where the great grim gods sit still in the dark,
And lamps burn dim at their carven feet,
And their eyes like the eyes of the serpent king
Flash green through the dusk of the incense sweet.

Though deep under ground I shall see the sun,
And shall feel the stretch of the blue overhead,
And the gems that gleam on the breast of the god.
And shall smell the scent of the peach—though dead.

Most of the world knew him only as Yung Le Ho, one
of the few white–haired Chinamen who were to be seen

about the streets of San Francisco. His cue was as long as that of any other John, and with the exception of wearing spectacles, he adhered strictly to his national costume. He sat all day long in an open bazaar where he worked in silk and ivory and sandal wood. Americans who had lived there long said he must be worth a vast deal of money, for Yung was the best workman in the city. All the ladies who were enthusiastic over Chinese art bought his painted silken birds, and beautiful lacquered boxes, his bronze vases, his little ivory gods and his carved sandal wood, and paid him whatsoever he demanded for them. Had he possessed a dozen hands he might have sold the work of all of them; as it was, he was very skillful with two. Yung was like Michel Angelo, he allowed no one to touch his work but himself; he did it all, rough work and delicate. When the ship brought him strange black boxes with a sweet spicy odor about them, he opened them with his own hands and took out the yellow ivory tusks, and the bales of silk, and the blocks of shining ebony. And no hands but his touched them until they were fashioned into the beautiful things with which the ladies of San Francisco loved to adorn their drawing rooms.

Day after day he sat in his stall, cross–legged and silent like the gods of his country, carving his ivory into strange images and his sandal wood into shapes of foliage and birds. Sometimes he cut it into the shapes of foliage of his own land; the mulberry and apricot and chestnut and juniper that grew about the sacred mountain; the bamboo and camphor tree, and the rich Indian bean, and the odorous camelias and japonicas that grew far to the south on the low banks of the Yang–Tse–Kiang. Sometimes he cut shapes and leaves that were not of earth, but were things he had seen in his dreams when the Smoke was on him.

There were some people beside the artistic public who knew Yung; they were the linguistic scholars of the city— there are a few of these, even so far west as San Francisco. The two or three men who knew a little Sanskrit and attacked an extract from the Vedas now and then, used often to go to Yung to get help. For the little white-haired Chinaman knew Sanskrit as thoroughly as his own tongue. The professors had a good deal of respect for Yung, though they never told anyone of it, and kept him completely obscured in the background as professors and doctors of philosophy always do persons whom they consider "doubtful" acquaintances. Yung never pushed himself forward, nor courted the learned gentlemen. He always gave them what they wanted, then shut up like a clam and no more could be gotten out of him. Perhaps Yung did not have quite as much respect for the gentlemen as they had for him. He had seen a good many countries and a good many people, and he knew knowledge from pedantry. He found American schoolmen distasteful. "Too muchee good to know muchee," he once sarcastically remarked. Of course Yung was only a heathen Chinee who bowed down to wood and stone, his judgment in this and other matters does not count for much.

There was one American whom Yung took to his heart and loved, if a Chinaman can love, and that was old Ponter. Ponter was one of the most learned men who ever drifted into 'Frisco, but his best days were over before he came. He had held the chair of Sanskrit in a western university for years, but he could drink too much beer and was too good a shot at billiards to keep that place forever, so the college has requested his resignation. He went from place to place until at last he drifted into San Francisco, where he stayed. He went clear down to the mud sills there. How he lived no one knew. He did some copying for the lawyers, and he waited on the table in a third–rate boarding house, and he smoked a great deal of opium. Yung, too, loved the Smoke; perhaps it was that as much as Sanskrit that drew the two men together. At any rate, as soon as Yung's bazaar was closed, they went together down to his dark litle den in the Chinese quarters, and there they talked Buddha and Confucius and Lau–tsz till midnight. Then they went across the hall to the Seven Portals of Paradise. There they each took a mat and each his own sweet pipe with bowls of jade and mouthpieces of amber—Yung had given Ponter one— and pulled a few steady puffs and were in bliss till morning.

To Ponter, Yung told a good deal of his history. Not in regular narrative form, for he never talked about himself long, but he let it out bit by bit. When he was a boy he lived in Nanking, the oldest city of the oldest empire, where the great schools are and the tallest pagoda in the world rears its height of shining porcelain. There he had been educated, and had learned all the wisdom of the Chinese. He became tired of all that after awhile; tired of the rice paper books and of the masters in their black gowns, of the blue mountains and of the shadows of the great tower that fell sharp upon the yellow pavement in the glare of the sun. He went south; down the great canal in a red barge with big sails like dragon's wings. He came to Soutcheofou that is built upon the water–ways among the hills of Lake Taihoo. There the air smelt always of flowers, and the bamboo woods were green, and the rice fields shook in the wind. There the actors and jugglers gather the year around, and the Mandrins come to find brides for their harems. For once a god had loved a woman of that city, and he gave to her the charms of heaven, and since then the maidens of Soutcheofou have been the most beautiful in the Middle Kingdom, and have lived but to love and be loved. There Yung dwelt until he tired of pleasure. Then he went on foot across the barren plains of Thibet and the snow–capped Himalyas into India. He spent ten years in a temple there among the Brahamin priests, learning the sacred books. Then he fell in with some high caste Indian magicians and went with them. Of the next five years of his life Yung never spoke. Once, when Ponter questioned him about them, he laughed an ugly laugh which showed his broken yellow teeth and said:

"I not know what I did then. The devil he know, he and the fiends."

At last Yung came to California. There he took to carving and the Smoke.

Yung was rich; he might have dwelt in a fine house, but he preferred to live among his own people in a little room across from the Seven Portals. He celebrated all the feasts and festivals with the other Chinamen, and bowed down to the gods in the joss house. He explained this to Ponter one day by saying:

"It is to keep us together, keep us Chinamen."

Wise Yung! It was not because of the cheapness of Chinese labor that the Chinese bill was enacted. It was because church and state feared this people who went about unproselyting and unproselyted. Who had printed centuries before Guttenberg was born, who had used anesthetics before chloroform was ever dreamed of. Who, in the new west, settled down and ate and drank and dressed as men had done in the days of the flood. Their

65

terrible antiquity weighed upon us like a dead hand upon a living heart.

Yung did not know much about English literature. He liked the Bible, and he had picked up a copy of Hiawatha and was very fond of it. I suppose the artificialness of the poem appealed to his natural instinct and his training. Ponter was much disgusted with his taste, and one night he read the whole of Hamlet aloud to him, translating the archaic phrases into doggeral Chinese as he read. When he finished, Yung stared at him with a troubled look and said in Chinese:

"Yes, it is a great book, but I do not understand. If I were a young man I might try, but it is different. We cut our trees into shape, we bind our women into shape, we make our books into shape by rule. Your trees and women and books just grow, and yet they have shape. I do not understand. Come, let us smoke, the Smoke is good."

Ponter threw the book on the floor and arose and paced the floor shouting angrily:

"O yes, d--n you! You are a terrible people! I have come as near losing all human feeling and all human kinship as ever a white man did, but you make me shudder, every one of you. You live right under the sun's face, but you cannot feel his fire. The breast of God heaves just over you, but you never know it. You ought to be a feeling, passionate people, but you are as heartless and devilish as your accursed stone gods that leer at you in your Pagodas. Your sages learn rites, rites, rites, like so many parrots. They have forgotten how to think so long ago that they have forgotten they ever forgot. Your drama has outlived pathos, your science has outlived investigation, your poetry has outlived passion. Your very roses do not smell, they have forgotten how to give odor ages and ages ago. Your devilish gods have cursed you with immortality and you have outlived your souls. You are so old that you are born yellow and wrinkled and blind. You ought to have been buried centuries before Europe was civilized. You ought to have been wrapped in your mort cloth ages before our swaddling clothes were made. You are dead things that move!"

Yung answered never a word, but smiled his hideous smile and went across to the Portals of Paradise, and lay down upon his mat, and drew long whiffs from his mouth piece, slowly, solemnly, as though he were doing sacrifice to some god. He dreams of his own country, dreams of the sea and the mountains and forests and the slopes of sunny land. When he awakes there is not much of his dream left, only masses and masses of color that haunt him all day.

"Ponter," said Yung one day as he sat cutting a little three-faced Vishnu in ivory, "when I die do not even bury me here. Let them go through the rites and then send me home. I must lie there while the flesh is yet on my bones. Let the funeral be grand. Let there be many mourners, and roast pigs, and rice and gin. Let the gin bowls be of real China, and let the coffin be a costly one like the coffins of Liauchau, there is money enough. Let my pipe stay in my hand, and put me on the first ship that sails."

Not long after that, Ponter arose from his mat one morning, and went over to waken Yung. But Yung would not waken any more. He had tasted his last ounce of the Smoke, and he lay with the mouthpiece in his mouth, and his fingers clutched about the bowl. Ponter sat down by him and said slowly:

"A white man has got pretty low down, Yung, when he takes to the Smoke and runs with a heathen. But I liked you, Yung, as much as a man can like a stone thing. You weren't a bad fellow, sir. You knew more Sanskrit than Muller dreamed of knowing, and more ethics than Plato, a long sight, and more black art than the devil himself. You knew more than any man I ever saw, more good and more evil. You could do a neater job with a knife and a piece of bone than any man in civilization, and you get away with more Smoke than any yaller man I ever saw. You were not a bad fellow Yung, but your heart has been dead these last six thousand years, and it was better for your carcass to follow suit."

He went out and got the finest lacquered coffin in 'Frisco and he put old Yung inside with a pound of rice and his pipe and a pound of the best opium in the market. Then he nailed him up singing: *"Ibimus, Ibimus, Utcumque praecedes, supernum, Carpere iter comites parati,"* softly as he hammered away.

He took the body to the graveyard where the Chinamen went through the rites. Then they loaded Yung on an outbound steamer. Next day Ponter stood on the docks and watched her plowing her way toward the Celestial shore.

Hesperian, XXII:6, Jan. 15, 1893, pp. 7–10

THE CLEMENCY OF THE COURT

"Damn you! What do you mean by giving me hooping like that?"

Serge Povolitchky folded his big, workworn hands and was silent. That helpless, doglike silence of his always had a bad effect on the guard's temper, and he turned on him afresh.

"What do you mean by it, I say? Maybe you think you are some better than the rest of us; maybe you think you are too good to work. We'll see about that."

Serge still stared at the ground, muttering in a low, husky voice, "I could make some broom, I think. I would try much."

"O, you would, would you? So you don't try now? We will see about that. We will send you to a school where you can learn to hoop barrels. We have a school here, a little, dark school, a night school, you know, where we teach men a great many things."

Serge looked up appealingly into the man's face and his eyelids quivered with terror, but he said nothing, so the guard continued:

"Now I'll sit down here and watch you hoop them barrels, and if you don't do a mighty good job, I'll report you to the warden and have you strung up as high as a rope can twist."

Serge turned to his work again. He did wish the guard would not watch him; it seemed to him that he could hoop all right if he did not feel the guard's eye on him all the time. His hands had never done anything but dig and plow and they were so clumsy he could not make them do right. The guard began to swear and Serge trembled so he could scarcely hold his hammer. He was very much afraid of the dark cell. His cell was next to it and often at night he had heard the men groaning and shrieking when the pain got bad, and begging the guards for water. He heard one poor fellow get delirious when the rope cut and strangled him, and talk to his mother all night long, begging her not to hug him so hard, for she hurt him.

The guard went out and Serge worked on, never even stopping to wipe the sweat from his face. It was strange he could not hoop as well as the other men, for he was as strong and stalwart as they, but he was so clumsy at it. He thought he could work in the broom room if they would only let him. He had handled straw all his life, and it would seem good to work at the broom corn that had the scent of outdoors about it. But they said the broom room was full. He felt weak and sick all over, someway. He could not work in the house, he had never been indoors a whole day in his life until he came here.

Serge was born in the western part of the State, where he did not see many people. His mother was a handsome Russian girl, one of a Russian colony that a railroad had brought West to build grades. His father was supposed to be a railroad contractor, no one knew surely. At any rate by no will of his own or wish of his own, Serge existed. When he was a few months old, his mother had drowned herself in a pond so small that no one ever quite saw how she managed to do it.

Baba Skaldi, an old Russian woman of the colony, took Serge and brought him up among her own children. A hard enough life he had of it with her. She fed him what her children would not eat, and clothed him in what her children would not wear. She used to boast to *baba* Konach that she got a man's work out of the young rat. There was one pleasure in Serge's life with her. Often at night after she had beaten him and he lay sobbing on the floor in the corner, she would tell her children stories of Russia. They were beautiful stories, Serge thought. In spite of all her cruelty he never quite disliked *baba* Skaldi because she could tell such fine stories. The story told oftenest was one about her own brother. He had done something wrong, Serge could never make out just what, and had been sent to Siberia. His wife had gone with him. The *baba* told all about the journey to Siberia as she had heard it from returned convicts; all about the awful marches in the mud and ice, and how on the boundary line the men would weep and fall down and kiss the soil of Russia. When her brother reached the prison, he and his wife used to work in the mines. His wife was too good a woman to get on well in the prison, the *baba* said, and one day she had been knouted to death at the command of an officer. After that her husband tried in many ways to kill himself, but they always caught him at it. At last, one night, he bit deep into his arm and tore open the veins with his teeth and bled to death. The officials found him dead with his teeth still set in his lacerated arm. When she finished the little boys used to cry out at the awfulness of it, but their mother would soothe them and tell them that such things could not possibly happen here, because in this country the State took care of people. In Russia there was no State, only the great Tzar. Ah, yes, the State would take care of the children! The *baba* had heard a Fourth-of-July speech once, and she had great ideas about the State.

Serge used to listen till his eyes grew big, and play that he was that brother of the *baba's* and that he had been knouted by the officials and that was why his little legs smarted so. Sometimes he would steal out in the snow in his bare feet and take a sunflower stalk and play he was hunting bears in Russia, or would walk about on the little frozen pond where his mother had died and think it was the Volga. Before his birth his mother used to go off alone and sit in the snow for hours to cool the fever in her head and weep and think about her own country. The feeling for the snow and the love for it seemed to go into the boy's blood, somehow. He was never so happy as when he saw the white flakes whirling.

When he was twelve years old a farmer took him to work for his board and clothes. Then a change came into Serge's life. That first morning he stood, awkward and embarrassed, in the Davis kitchen, holding his hands under his hat and shuffling his bare feet over the floor, a little yellow cur came up to him and began to rub its nose against his leg. He held out his hand and the dog licked it. Serge bent over him, stroking him and calling him Russian pet names. For the first time in his lonely, loveless life, he felt that something liked him.

The Davises gave him enough to eat and enough to wear and they did not beat him. He could not read or talk English, so they treated him very much as they did the horses. He stayed there seven years because he did not have sense enough to know that he was utterly mis-

erable and could go somewhere else, and because the
Slavonic instinct was in him to labor and keep silent. The
dog was the only thing that made life endurable. He
called the dog Matushka, which was the name by which
he always thought of his mother. He used to go to town
sometimes, but he did not enjoy it, people frightened
him so. When the town girls used to pass him dressed
in their pretty dresses with their clean, white hands, he
thought of his bare feet and his rough, tawny hair and
his ragged overalls, and he would slink away behind his
team with Matushka. On the coldest winter nights he
always slept in the barn with the dog for a bedfellow.
As he and the dog cuddled up to each other in the hay,
he used to think about things, most often about Russia and
the State. Russia must be a fine country but he was glad
he did not live there, because the State was much better.
The State was so very good to people. Once a man came
there to get Davis to vote for him, and he asked Serge
who his father was. Serge said he had none. The man
only smiled and said, "Well, never mind, the State will
be a father to you, my lad, and a mother."

Serge had a vague idea that the State must be an abstract thing of some kind, but he always thought of her
as a woman with kind eyes, dressed in white with a
yellow light about her head, and a little child in her
arms, like the picture of the virgin in the church. He
always took off his hat when he passed the court house
in town, because he had an idea that it had something
to do with the State someway. He thought he owed the
State a great deal for something, he did not know what;
that the State would do something great for him some
day, because he had no one else. After his chores he used
to go and sit down in the corral with his back against
the wire fence and his chin on his knees and look at the

sunset. He never got much pleasure out of it, it was always like watching something die. It made him feel desolute and lonesome to see so much sky, yet he always sat there, irresistibly fascinated. It was not much wonder that his eyes grew dull and his brain heavy, sitting there evening after evening with his dog, staring across the brown, windswept prairies that never lead anywhere, but always stretch on and on in a great yearning for something they never reach. He liked the plains because he thought they must be like the Russian steppes, and because they seemed like himself, always lonely and empty-handed.

One day when he was helping Davis top a hay stack, Davis got angry at the dog for some reason and kicked at it. Serge threw out his arm and caught the blow himself. Davis, angrier than before, caught the hatchet and laid the dog's head open. He threw down the bloody hatchet and telling Serge to go clean it, he bent over his work. Serge stood motionless, as dazed and helpless as if he had been struck himself. The dog's tail quivered and its legs moved weakly, its breath came through its throat in faint, wheezing groans and from its bleeding head its two dark eyes, clouded with pain, still looked lovingly up at him. He dropped on his knees beside it and lifted its poor head against his heart. It was only for a moment. It laid its paw upon his arm and then was still. Serge laid the dog gently down and rose. He took the bloody hatchet and went up behind his master. He did not hurry and he did not falter. He raised the weapon and struck down, clove through the man's skull from crown to chin, even as the man had struck the dog. Then he went to the barn to get a shovel to bury the dog. As he passed the house, the woman called out to him to tell her husband to come to dinner. He answered simply,

"He will not come to dinner today. I killed him behind the haystack."

She rushed from the house with a shriek and when she caught sight of what lay behind the hay-stack, she started for the nearest farm house. Serge went to the barn for the shovel. He had no consciousness of having done wrong. He did not even think about the dead man. His heart seemed to cling to the side of his chest, the only thing he had ever loved was dead. He went to the hay-mow where he and Matushka slept every night and took a box from under the hay from which he drew a red silk handkerchief, the only "pretty thing," and indeed, the only handkerchief he had ever possessed. He went back to the hay-stack and never once glancing at the man, took the dog in his arms.

There was one spot on the farm that Serge liked. He and Matushka used often to go there on Sundays. It was a little, marshy pool, grown up in cat-tails and reeds with a few scraggy willows on the banks. The grass used to be quite green there, not red and gray like the buffalo grass. There he carried Matushka. He laid him down and began to dig a grave under the willows. The worst of it was that the world went on just as usual. The winds were laughing away among the rushes, sending the water slapping against the banks. The meadow larks sang in the corn field and the sun shone just as it did yesterday and all the while Matushka was dead and his own heart was breaking in his breast. When the hole was deep enough, he took the handkerchief from his pocket and tied it neatly about poor Matushka's mangled head. Then he pulled a few wild roses and laid them on its breast and fell sobbing across the body of the little yellow cur. Presently he saw the neighbors coming over the hill with

Mrs. Davis, and he laid the dog in the grave and covered him up.

About his trial Serge remembered very little, except that they had taken him to the court house and he had not found the State. He remembered that the room was full of people, and some of them talked a great deal, and that the young lawyer who defended him cried when his sentence was read. That lawyer seemed to understand it all, about Matushka and the State, and everything. Serge thought he was the handsomest and most learned man in the world. He had fought day and night for Serge, without sleeping and almost without eating. Serge could always see him as he looked when he paced up and down the platform, shaking the hair back from his brow and trying to get it through the heads of the jurymen that love was love, even if it was for a dog. The people told Serge that his sentence had been commuted from death to imprisonment for life by the clemency of the court, but he knew well enough that it was by the talk of that lawyer. He had not deserted Serge after the trial even, he had come with him to the prison and had seen him put on his convict clothing.

"It's the State's badge of knighthood, Serge," he said, bitterly, touching one of the stripes. "The old emblem of the royal garter, to show that your blood is royal."

Just as the six o'clock whistle was blowing, the guard returned.

"You are to go to your cell tonight, and if you don't do no better in the morning, you are to be strung up in the dark cell, come along."

Serge laid down his hammer and followed him to his cell. Some of the men made little book shelves for their cells and pasted pictures on the walls. Serge had neither books nor pictures, and he did not know how to ask for any, so his cell was bare. The cells were only six by four, just a little larger than a grave.

As a rule, the prisoners suffered from no particular cruelty, only from the elimination of all those little delicacies that make men men. The aim of the prison authorities seemed to be to make everything unnecessarily ugly and repulsive. The little things in which fine feeling is most truly manifest received no respect at all. Serge's bringing up had been none of the best, but it took him some time to get used to eating without knife or fork the indifferent food thrust in square tin bowls under the door of his cell. Most of the men read at night, but he could not read, so he lay tossing on his iron bunk, wondering how the fields were looking. His greatest deprivation was that he could not see the fields. The love of the plains was strong in him. It had always been so, ever since he was a little fellow, when the brown grass was up to his shoulders and the straw stacks were the golden mountains of fairyland. Men from the cities on the hills never understand this love, but the men from the plain country know what I mean. When he had tired himself out with longing, he turned over and fell asleep. He was never impatient, for he believed that the State would come some day and explain, and take him to herself. He watched for her coming every day, hoped for it every night.

In the morning the work went no better. They watched him all the time and he could do nothing. At noon they took him into the dark cell and strung him up. They put his arms behind him and tied them together, then passed the rope about his neck, drawing arms up as high as they could be stretched, so that if he let them "sag" he would strangle, and so they left him. The cell was perfectly bare and was not long enough for a man to lie at full length in. The prisoners were told to stand up, so Serge stood. At night his arms were let down long enough for him to eat his bread and water, then he was roped up again. All night long he stood there. By the end of the next day the pain in his arms was almost unendurable. They were paralyzed from the shoulder down so that the guard had to feed him like a baby. The next day and the next night and the next day he lay upon the floor of the cell, suffering as though every muscle were being individually wrenched from his arms. He had not been out of the bare cell for four days. All the ventilation came through some little augur holes in the door and the heat and odor were becoming unbearable. He had thought on the first night that the pain would kill him before morning, but he had endured over eighty-four hours of it and when the guard came in with his bread and water he found him lying with his eyes closed and his teeth set on his lip. He roused him with a kick and held the bread and water out to him, but Serge took only the water.

"Rope too tight?" growled the guard. Serge said nothing. He was almost dead now and he wanted to finish for he could not hoop barrels.

"Gittin so stuck up you can't speak, are you? Well, we'll just stretch you up a bit tighter." And he gave the stick in the rope another vicious twist that almost tore the arms from their sockets and sent a thrill of agony through the man's whole frame. Then Serge was left alone. The fever raged in his veins and about midnight his thirst was intolerable. He lay with his mouth open and his tongue hanging out. The pain in his arms made his whole body tremble like a man with a chill. He could no longer keep his arms up and the ropes were beginning to strangle him. He did not call for help. He had heard poor devils shriek for help all night long and get no relief. He suffered, as the people of his mother's nation, in hopeless silence. The blood of the serf was in him, blood that has cowered beneath the knout for centuries and uttered no complaint. Then the State would surely come soon, she would not let them kill him. His mother, the State!

He fell into a half stupor. He dreamed about what the *baba* used to tell about the bargemen in their bearskin coats coming down the Volga in the spring when the ice had broken up and gone out; about how the wolves used to howl and follow the sledges across the snow in the starlight. That cold, white snow, that lay in ridges and banks! He thought he felt it in his mouth and he awoke and found himself licking the stone floor. He thought how lovely the plains would look in the morning when the sun was up; how the sunflowers would shake themselves in the wind, how the corn leaves would shine and how the cob-webs would sparkle all over the grass and the air would be clear and blue, the birds would begin to sing, the colts would run and jump in the pasture and the black bull would begin to bellow for his corn.

The rope grew tighter and tighter. The State must come soon now. He thought he felt the dog's cold nose against his throat. He tried to call its name, but the sound only came in an inarticulate gurgle. He drew his knees up to his chin and died.

And so it was that this great mother, the State, took this willful, restless child of her's and put him to sleep in her bosom.

Hesperian, XXII:17, Oct. 26, 1893, pp. 3–7

A NIGHT AT GREENWAY COURT

I, Richard Morgan, of the town of Winchester, county of Frederick, of the Commonwealth of Virginia, having been asked by my friend Josiah Goodrich, who purports making a history of this valley, to set down all I know concerning the death of M. Philip Marie Maurepas, a gentleman, it seems, of considerable importance in his own country, will proceed to do so briefly and with what little skill I am master of.

The incident which I am about to relate occurred in my early youth, but so deeply did it fix itself upon my memory that the details are as clear as though it had happened but yesterday. Indeed, of all the stirring events that have happened in my time, those nights spent at Greenway Court in my youth stand out most boldly in my memory. It was, I think, one evening late in October, in the year 1752, that my Lord Fairfax sent his man over to my father's house at Winchester to say that on the morrow his master desired my company at the Court. My father, a prosperous tobacco merchant, greatly regretted that I should be brought up in a new country, so far from the world of polite letters and social accomplishments, and contrived that I should pass much of my leisure in the company of one of the most gracious gentlemen and foremost scholars of his time, Thomas, Lord Fairfax. Accordingly, I was not surprised at my lord's summons. Late in the afternoon of the following day I rode over to the Court, and was first shown into my lord's private office, where for some time we discussed my lord's suit, then pending with the sons of Joist Hite, concerning certain lands beyond the Blue Ridge, then held by them, which my lord claimed through the extension of his grant from the crown. Our business being dispatched, he said:

"Come, Richard, in the hall I will present you to some gentlemen who will entertain you until supper time. There is a Frenchman stopping here, M. Maurepas, a gentleman of most engaging conversation. The Viscount Chillingham you will not meet until later, as he has gone out with the hounds."

We crossed the yard and entered the hall where the table was already laid with my lord's silver platters and thin glass goblets, which never ceased to delight me when I dined with him, and though since, in London, I have drunk wine at a king's table, I have seen none finer. At the end of the room by the fireplace sat two men over their cards. One was a clergyman, whom I had met before, the other a tall spare gentleman whom my lord introduced as M. Philip Marie Maurepas. As I sat down, the gentleman addressed me in excellent English. The bright firelight gave me an excellent opportunity for observing this man, which I did, for with us strangers were too few not to be of especial interest, and in a way their very appearance spoke to us of an older world beyond the seas for which the hearts of all of us still hungered.

He was, as I have said, a tall man, narrow chested and with unusually long arms. His forehead was high and his chin sharp, his skin was dark, tanned, as I later learned, by his long service in the Indes. He had a pair of restless black eyes and thin lips shaded by a dark mustache. His hair was coal black and grew long upon his shoulders; later I noticed that it was slightly touched with gray. His dress had once been fine, but had seen considerable service and was somewhat the worse for the weather. He wore breeches of dark blue velvet and leather leggins. His shirt and vest were of dark red and had once been worked with gold.

In his belt he wore a long knife with a slender blade and a handle of gold curiously worked in the form of a serpent, with eyes of pure red stones which sparkled mightily in the firelight. I must confess that in the very appearance of this man there was something that both interested and attracted me, and I fell to wondering what strange sights those keen eyes of his had looken upon.

"M. Maurepas intends spending the winter in our wilderness, Richard, and I fear he will find that our woods offer a cold welcome to a stranger."

"Well, my lord, all the more to my taste. Having seen how hot the world can be, I am willing to see how cold."

"To see that, sir," said I, "you should go to Quebeck where I have been with trappers. There I have thrown a cup full of water in the air and seen it descend solid ice."

"I fear it will be cold enough here for my present attire," said he laughing, "yet it may be that I will taste the air of Quebeck before quitting this wilderness of yours."

My lord then excused himself and withdrew, leaving me alone with the gentlemen.

"Come join me in a game of hazard, Master Morgan; it is yet half an hour until supper time," said the clergy-man, who had little thought for anything but his cards and his dinner.

"And I will look at the portraits; you have fleeced me quite enough for one day, good brother of the Church. I have nothing left but my diamond that I cut from the hand of a dead Rajpoot, finger and all, and it is a lucky stone, and I have no mind to lose it."

"With your permission, M. Maurepas, I will look at the portraits with you, as I have no mind to play to-night; besides I think this is the hour for Mr. Courtney's devotions," said I, for I had no liking for the fat churchman. He, like so many of my lord's guests, was in a sense a refugee from justice; having fallen into disgrace with the heads of the English church, he had fled to our country and sought out Lord Halifax, whose door was closed against no man. He had been there then three months, dwelling in shameful idleness, one of that band of rene-gades who continually ate at my lord's table and hunted with his dogs and devoured his substance, waiting for some turn of fortune, like the suitors in the halls of Pen-elope. So we left the clergyman counting his gains and repaired to the other end of the hall, where, above the mahogany bookcases, the portraits hung. Of these there were a considerable number, and I told the Frenchman the names of as many as I knew. There was my lord's father and mother, and his younger brother, to whom he had given his English estate. There was his late majesty George I., and old Firnando Fairfax. Hanging under the dark picture of the king he had deposed and yet loved was Firnando's son, fighting Thomas Fairfax, third Lord

and Baron of Cameron, the great leader of the common-
ers with Cromwell, who rode after Charles at Heyworth
Moore and thrust the people's petition in the indignant
monarch's saddle bow; who defeated the king's forces at
Naseby, and after Charles was delivered over to the com-
missioners of Parliament, met him at Nottingham and
kissed his fallen sovereign's hand, refusing to sit in judgment over God's anointed.

Among these pictures there was one upon which I had
often gazed in wonderment. It was the portrait of a lady,
holding in her hand a white lily. Some heavy instrument
had been thrust through the canvas, marring the face
beyond all recognition, but the masses of powdered hair,
and throat and arms were enough to testify to the beauty
of the original. The hands especially were of surpassing
loveliness, and the thumb was ornamented with a single
emerald, as though to call attention to its singular perfection. The costume was the court dress of the then
present reign, and with the eagerness of youthful imag-
ination I had often fancied that could that picture speak
it might tell something of that upon which all men wondered; why, in the prime of his manhood and success at
court, Lord Fairfax had left home and country, friends,
and all that men hold dear, renounced the gay society in
which he had shone and his favorite pursuit of letters, and
buried himself in the North American wilderness. Upon
this canvas the Frenchman's eye was soon fixed.

"And this?" he asked.

"I do not know, sir; of that my lord has never told me."

"Well, let me see; what is a man's memory good for,
if not for such things? I must have seen those hands
before, and that coronet."

He looked at it closely and then stood back and looked

at it from a distance. Suddenly an exclamation broke from him, and a sharp light flashed over his features.

"Ah, I thought so! So your lord has never told you of this, *parbleau, il a beaucoup de cause!* Look you, my boy, that emerald is the only beautiful thing that ever came out of Herrenhausen—that, and she who wears it. Perhaps you will see that emerald, too, some day; how many and how various they will yet be, God alone knows. How long, O Lord, how long? as your countrymen say."

So bitter was his manner that I was half afraid, yet had a mind to question him, when my lord returned. He brought with him a young man of an appearance by no means distinguished, yet kindly and affable, whom he introduced as the Viscount Chillingham.

"You've a good country here, Master Norton, and better sport than we, for all our game laws. Hang laws, I say, they're naught but a trouble to them that make 'em and them that break 'em, and its little good they do any of us. My lord, you must sell me your deer hound, Fanny, I want to take her home with me, and show 'em what your dogs are made of over here."

"You are right welcome to her, or any of the pack."

At this juncture my lord's housekeeper, Mistress Crawford, brought in the silver candlesticks, and the servants smoking dishes of bear's meat and venison, and many another delicacy for which my lord's table was famous, besides French wines and preserved cherries from his old estates in England.

The viscount flung himself into his chair, still flushed from his chase after the hounds, and stretched his long limbs.

"This is a man's life you have here, my lord. I tell you, you do well to be away from London now; it's as dull there as Mr. Courtney's church without its spiritual pastor."

The clergyman lifted his eyes from his venison long enough to remark slyly, "Or as Hampton Court without its cleverest gamester," at which the young man reddened under his fresh coat of tan, for he had been forced to leave England because of some gaming scandal which cast grave doubts upon his personal honor.

The talk drifted to the death of the queen of Denmark, the king's last visit to Hanover, and various matters of court gossip. Of these the gentlemen spoke freely, more freely, perhaps, than they would have dared do at home. As I have said, my lord's guests were too often gentlemen who had left dark histories behind them, and had fled into the wilds where law was scarce more than a name and man had to contend only with the savage condition of nature, and a strong arm stood in better stead than a tender conscience. I have met many a strange man at Greenway Court, men who had cheated at play, men who had failed in great political plots, men who fled from a debtor's prison, and men charged with treason, and with a price upon their heads. For in some respects Lord Fairfax was a strangely conservative man, slow to judge and slow to anger, having seen much of the world, and thinking its conditions hard and its temptations heavy, deeming, I believe, all humanity more sinned against than sinning. And yet I have seldom known his confidence to be misplaced or his trust to be ill repaid. Whatever of information I may have acquired in my youth, I owe to the conversation of these men, for about my lord's board exiles and outlaws of all nations gathered, and unfolded in the friendly solitude of the wilderness plots and intrigues then scarce known in Europe.

On all the matters that were discussed the Frenchman

seemed the best versed man present, even touching the most minute details of the English court. At last the viscount, who was visibly surprised, turned upon him sharply.

"Have you been presented at court, monsieur?"

"Not in England, count, but I have seen something of your king in Hanover; there, I think, on the banks of the stupid Leine, is his proper court, and 'tis there he sends the riches of your English. But in exchange I hear that he has brought you his treasure of Herrenhausen in her private carriage with a hundred postilions to herald her advent."

His eyes were fixed keenly on my lord's face, but Fairfax only asked coldly:

"And where, monsieur, have you gained so perfect a mastery of the English tongue?"

"At Madras, your lordship, under Bourdonnais, where I fought your gallant countrymen, high and low, for the empire of the Indes. They taught me the sound of English speech well enough, and the music of English swords."

"Faith," broke in the viscount, "then they taught you better than they know themselves, though it's their mother tongue. You've seen hot service there, I warrant?"

"Well, what with English guns sweeping our decks by sea, and the Indian sun broiling our skin by land, and the cholera tearing our entrails, we saw hot service indeed."

"Were you in the Indian service after the return of Governor Bourdonnais to France, M. Maurepas?"

"After his return to the Bastile, you mean, my lord. Yes, I was less fortunate than my commander. There are worse prisons on earth than the Bastile, and Madras is one of them. When France sends a man to the Indes she has no intention he shall return alive. How I did so is another matter. Yes, I served afterward under Duplix, who seized Bourdonnais' troops as well as his treasure. I was with him in the Deccan when he joined his troops with Murzapha Jung against the Nabob of the Carnatic, and white men were set to fight side by side with heathen. And I say to you, gentlemen, that the bravest man in all that melée was the old Nabob himself. He was a hundred and seven years old, and he had been a soldier from his mother's knee. He was mounted on the finest elephant in the Indian army, and he led his soldiers right up into the thick of the fight in full sweep of the French bullets, ordering his body-guard back and attended only by his driver. And when he saw his old enemy, Tecunda Sahib in the very midst of the French guards, he ordered his driver to up and at him, and he prodded the beast forward with his own hand. When the beast came crashing through our lines a bullet struck the old man in the breast, but still he urged him on. And when the elephant was stopped the driver was gone and the old Nabob was stone dead, sitting bolt upright in his curtained cage with a naked scimetar in his hand, ready for his vengeance. And I tell ye now, gentlemen, that I for one was right sorry that the bullet went home, for I am not the man who would see a brave soldier balked of his revenge."

It is quite impossible with the pen to give any adequate idea of the dramatic manner in which he related this. I think it stirred the blood of more than one of us. The viscount struck the table with his hand and cried:

"That's talking, sir; you see the best of life, you French. As for us, we are so ridden by king–craft and state–craft we are as good as dead men. Between Walpole and the little German we have forgot the looks of a sword, and we never hear a gun these times but at the christening of some brat or other."

The clergyman looked up reproachfully from his preserved cherries, and Lord Fairfax, who seldom suffered any talk that savored of disloyalty, rose to his feet and lifted his glass.

"Gentlemen, the king's health."

"The king's health," echoed we all rising. But M. Maurepas sat stiff in his chair, and his glass stood full beside him. The viscount turned upon him fiercely.

"Monsieur, you do not drink the king's health?"

"No, sir; your king, nor my king, nor no man's king. I have no king. May the devil take them one and all! and that's my health to them."

"Monsieur," cried my lord sternly, "I am surprised to hear a soldier of the king of France speak in this fashion."

"Yes, my lord, I have been a soldier of the king, and I know the wages of kings. What were they for Bourdonnais, the bravest general who ever drew a sword? The Bastile! What were they for all my gallant comrades? Cholera, massacre, death in the rotting marshes of Pondicherry. *Le Diable!* I know them well; prison, the sword, the stake, the recompense of kings." He laughed terribly and struck his forehead with his hand.

"Monsieur," said my lord, "It may be that you have suffered much, and for that reason only do I excuse much that you say. Human justice is often at fault, and kings are but human. Nevertheless, they are ordained of heaven, and so long as there is breath in our bodies we owe them loyal service."

The Frenchman rose and stood, his dark eyes flashing like coals of fire and his hands trembling as he waved them in the air. And methought the prophets of Israel must have looked so when they cried out unto the people, though his words were as dark blasphemy as ever fell from human lips.

"I tell you, sir, that the day will come and is now at hand when there will be no more kings. When a king's blood will be cheaper than pothouse wine and flow as plentifully. When crowned heads will pray for a peasant's cap, and princes will hide their royal lineage as lepers hide their sores. Ordained of God! Look you, sir, there is a wise man of France, so wise indeed that he dares not dwell in France, but hides among the Prussians, who says that there is no God! No Jehovah with his frying pan of lost souls! That it is all a tale made up by kings to terrify their slaves; that instead of God making kings, the kings made God."

We were all struck with horror and the viscount rose to his feet again and threw himself into an attitude of attack, while Mr. Courtney, whose place it was to speak, cowered in his seat and continued to look wistfully at the cherries.

"Stop, sir," bawled the viscount, "we have not much faith left in England, thanks to such as Mr. Courtney here, but we've enough still to fight for. Little George may have his faults, but he's a brave man and a soldier. Let us see whether you can be as much."

But the Frenchman did not so much as look at him. He was well sped with wine, and in his eyes there was a fierce light as of some ancient hatred woke anew. Staggering down the hall he pointed to the canvas which had so interested him in the afternoon.

"My lord, I wonder at you, that you should dare to keep that picture here, though three thousand miles of perilous sea, and savagery, and forests, and mountains impassible lie between you and Hampton Court. If you are a man, I think you have no cause to love the name of king. Yet, is not your heart as good as any man's, and will not your money buy as many trinkets? I tell you, this wilderness is not dark enough to hide that woman's face! And she carries a lily in her hand, the lilies of Herrenhausen! *Justice de Dieu*—" but he got no further, for my lord's hand had struck him in the mouth.

It all came about so quickly that even then it was but a blur of sudden action to me. We sprang between them, but Fairfax had no intention of striking twice.

"We can settle this in the morning, sir," he said quietly. As he turned away M. Maurepas drew himself together with the litheness of a cat, and before I could catch his arm he had seized the long knife from his belt and thrown it after his host. It whizzed past my lord and stuck quivering in the oak wainscoting, while the man who threw it sank upon the floor a pitiable heap of intoxication. My lord turned to his man, who still stood behind his chair. "Henry, call me at five; at six I shall kill a scoundrel."

With that he left us to watch over the drunken slumbers of the Frenchman.

In the morning they met on the level stretch before the court. At my lord's request I stood as second to M. Maurepas. My principal was much shaken by his debauch of last night, and I thought when my lord looked upon him he was already dead. For in Lord Fairfax's face was a purpose which it seemed no human will could thwart. Never have I seen him look the noble, Christian gentleman as he looked it then. Just as the autumn mists were rising from the hills, their weapons crossed, and the rising sun shot my lord's blade with fire until it looked the sword of righteousness indeed. It lasted but a moment. M. Maurepas, so renowned in war and gallantry, who had been the shame of two courts and the

91

rival of two kings, fell, unknown and friendless, in the wilderness.

Two years later, after I had been presented and, through my father, stood in favor at court, I once had the honor to dine with his majesty at Hampton Court. At his right sat a woman known to history only too well; still brilliant, still beautiful, as she was unto the end. By her side I was seated. When the dishes were removed, as we sat over our wine, the king bade me tell him some of the adventures that had befallen in my own land.

"I can tell you, your majesty, how Lord Fairfax fought and killed M. Maurepas about a woman's picture."

"That sounds well, tell on," said the monarch in his heavy accent.

Then upon my hand under the table I felt a clasp, cold and trembling. I glanced down and saw there a white hand of wondrous beauty, the thumb ornamented with a single emerald. I sat still in amazement, for the lady's face was smiling and gave no sign.

The king clinked his glass impatiently with his nail.

"Well, go on with your story. Are we to wait on you all day?"

Again I felt that trembling pressure in mute entreaty on my hand.

"I think there is no story to tell, your majesty."

"And I think you are a very stupid young man," said his majesty testily, as he rose from the table.

"Perhaps he is abashed," laughed my lady, but her bosom heaved with a deep sigh of relief.

So my day of royal favor was a short one, nor was I sorry, for I had kept my friend's secret and shielded a fair lady's honor, which are the two first duties of a Virginian.

Nebraska Literary Magazine, June, 1896

DAILY DIALOGUES

OR, CLOAK ROOM CONVERSATION AS OVERHEARD BY THE TIRED LISTENER.

Place:—West end of University Hall, first floor.
Time:—Five days in the week.

DIALOGUE I.

Gladys Lynn, Calypso Klingenspohr.

CALYPSO: "Quick, Gladys, get the other Gamma Gamma Lambda girls. What shall we do? There is that new girl that we want, Lavender Lathrop, cornered by a whole gang of those Delta Lambdas."

GLADYS: "Horrid things. They think they are just too smart for any use because they got more invitations to the next Psi party than Our Girls did. Never mind, Psyclonia Stevens is going to give a party real soon, and she says she shant invite one of them."

CALYPSO: "Serve them just right. But we mustn't let them have Lavender or they will be worse than ever. I don't think much of their new initiates anyway. That Ethelberta Sidles is a perfect stick, and that Miss O'Hoolihan that they are so proud of getting and who refused—"

GLADYS: "Why Calypso! You know that's not so at all. It was all a mistake, and we never really wanted her. She was asked without the consent of the whole sorority. We wouldn't have her, the stuckup thing, and so I told one of the Lambda girls, the other day, when they asked me to con—"

CALYPSO: "But Gladys, just look how they have fastened on to Lavender—five of them—as affectionate as if they had known her six semesters. What in the world shall we do? They were flocking around her like that at gymnasium yesterday."

GLADYS: "I'll go and ask her where the Latin lesson is, and try to bring her over here. We will have to get in our work on her awfully quick, and the sooner the better. Calypso, you write a nice hand, you will be the one to write the letter to her mother about a fraternity being 'a monument for good,' about the number of celebrated Gamma Gamma Lambda girls, including Julia Ward Howe, Mrs. Lease, Dr. Mary Walker, and the rest, and especially about the benefits of belonging to an 'exclusive circle' like the Gamma Gamma Lambda, whose members are the especial pets of the Profs. We will take her into chapel to-day and sit on both sides of her. To-morrow we will all go and call on her. They say the Delta Lambdas have been to call on her already in a body, and, you know, I am the only one of us that has gone. How I wish Psyclonia was here. She is our best talker. We *must* keep Lavender away from those Delta Lambdas."

DIALOGUE II.

Gladys Lynn, Calypso Klingenspohr, Lavender Lathrop.

GLADYS: "Come over here, and some of *Our* Girls will help you with your Latin. I do so want you to meet Calypso Klingenspohr. She is one of our smartest girls. —Calypso, dearest, this is Lavender Lathrop, that I was speaking to you about—I think Lavender is such a *sweet* name."

CALYPSO, *(Kissing her)*: "I'm just charmed to meet you, Lavender. I feel as if I had known you years and years already."

GLADYS: "Now if Circe was only here, Circe O'Rourke, you know. She is one of the Sweetest Girls in our fraternity. She is awfully popular, too—one of the Zeta boys walked home with her one day last week."

CALYPSO: "Yes, and you ought to see her new party dress, girlie. It's too lovely for anything. There isn't a dress to equal it in that whole Delta Lambda fraternity. They boasted so much about that Sidles girl's graduating dress—'so complete,' you know—red dress, fan, sash, slippers, stockings, gloves and hair—but I know it's nothing to Circe's new one. It's been the talk of Our Fraternity for weeks. You ought to see it."

LAVENDER: "I am sure I should like to very much. What is it made of?"

CALYPSO, *(glibly)*: "Pale green surah, with canary colored trimmings, and old gold sash, made Empire, with Medici collar, cut V neck, and *en train,* Watteau pleat in the back, and *jabot* of real lace shirred down the front in cascades."

GLADYS: "She got it for the next Psi party. She and I both got invitations. You know we are usually the belles. Perhaps sometime you will be invited too, Lavender dear, if *(Putting her arms around her)* you should ever be a Gamma Gamma Lambda. I'm going to introduce you to some of the Psi boys after chapel. They are the flyest boys in the University, and you know we are right in with them. Once one of Our Girls married a Psi—she was a lovely girl, too—and she has been quite like a mother to them ever since."

CALYPSO: "If it was only last year, Lavender could go alright. We could give one of our leap year parties.

We gave them regularly last year, and had a leap year card club where we entertained our young gentlemen friends."

GLADYS: "Yes, and Circe got the prize. I do so wish she was here. I am sure you will like her."

CALYPSO: "I think I know where she is, Gladys darling, and I'll go and look for her. I'm almost sure I saw her talking with Eric Gustafson—he's the new Zeta, you know, Lavender—in the hall." *(Going)*.

GLADYS: "Calypso is such a *sweet* girl. And she's awfully smart, too. She always get a hundred. They say she's the best in Shakespeare, and she thinks Macbeth is awfully cute."

LAVENDER: "The best? Why, some one that was in the class told me that Miss Klingenspohr was not very good."

GLADYS: "That must have been one of those horrid barbs. They are so *envious*. I know Calypso is good because Circe told me so, and because she is the smartest girl in Our Fraternity. Besides, I know that she always crams up on the Shakespeare references in the library, and knows Mrs. Jameson's Shakespeare's Heroines by heart. But here she comes again."

DIALOGUE III.

Gladys Lynn, Calypso Klingenspohr, Lavender Lathrop, Psyclonia Stevens.

CALYPSO: "Circe O'Rourke *was* talking with Mr. Gustafson, and she wouldn't come away. I found Psyclonia, though. Psyclonia graduated last year, you know, Lavender, and posts in—"

PSYCLONIA: "Lavender? By Jinks you must be the Lavender Lathrop that Gladys was talking about at Our last meeting. Tickled to death to know you. Shake on it.

Good gracious! I almost forgot and gave you the Gamma
Gamma Lambda grip!"

GLADYS: "Where have you been, dearest? We were
hoping you would come for some time."

PSYCLONIA: "Out in the hall having a gay old time
with Frankie. I'm almost sure that if Cal here hadn't
come and taken me away, he would have asked me to
ice cream."

GLADYS: "Frank Freshlet is another of the Zeta boys,
Lavender."

LAVENDER: "Ice cream?"

PSYCLONIA: "Cert! I remember Georgie Jones took
me to ice cream once, two years ago. The frat boys sometimes *do* take us, when it gets towards spring."

CALYPSO: *(aside to Lavender)* "Psyclonia has awfully
taking ways with the boys. She has been engaged seven
times, and not all *this* leap year either."

PSYCLONIA: "By the way, Lavvy, I hear you attended one of those antiquated literary societies last Friday. How in the world did you stand it, to meet *all sorts*
of people? You know they aren't a bit *exclusive,* and I
suppose they introduced about 'steen dozen countrys to
you, and made you listen to a rocky literary program. You
ought to hear the programs at some of the Gamma Gamma Lambda meetings. We *do* have them sometimes, and
you can bet they are corkers."

GLADYS: "Yes. Calypso and I are going to read
papers at our next meeting."

LAVENDER: "Is that what you were writing from
those magazines yesterday, when you wouldn't tell me?"

GLADYS: "And—and Circe is going to read one just
as quick as she gets back her 'Incident in my Summer
Vacation,' and Psyclonia read one once last year, and—
and O Psyclonia, did you know that the last numbers of

the *Lock* were out? Circe got them this morning, and is going to distribute them to Our Chapter during chapel time."

PSYCLONIA: "Did you ever show Lavvy any copies of the *Lock,* sister?"

GLADYS: "No, I haven't yet. Where is that last year's copy that you usually have with you, Calypso darling?"

PSYCLONIA: "The *Lock* is a bang–up literary magazine published monthly by Our Fraternity. It is edited now by Epsilon, one of our flyest chapters.—Here, Honey, read Lavender the monthly letter from Our Chapter in this number. It don't matter if it is a last year's copy."

GLADYS *(reads):* "Eastern Gamma Gamma Lambda girls will be glad to know that Mu Chapter is valiantly holding its own, and may still boast that its members are the belles of the University and the darlings of the Faculty. In the past month we have initiated one new member, secured in the teeth of the other girls' fraternity, the Delta Lambda, which has a straggling chapter here."

"One of the most prominent events of the season, and one which aroused high interest in University circles, occurred on the evening of February 31, when the palatial mansion of Calypso Klingenspohr on Packinghouse Avenue was thrown open to a brilliant gathering. The occasion was a leap year party given by the ladies of Mu Chapter of Gamma Gamma Lambda to friends and admirers. The beautiful home of Miss Klingenspohr, who by the way is one of the most charming of our society buds, was tastefully decorated, and the hours from nine to twelve were spent in the delightful recreations of cards and dancing, interrupted by the serving of dainty refreshments, consisting of lemonade and delicious wafers. The royal prizes were won by Mr. Gustafson and Miss

O'Rourke, and the boobies by Mr. Freshlet and Miss Lynn."

PSYCLONIA: "There, Lavender. That's the kind of a sorority the Gamma Gamma Lambda is. They are a mighty stunning set. Why, I remember that some of the finest jewelry in school was worn by a prominent alumna of Our Chapter, Rebecca Isaacstein, now of Bryn Mawr. The Delta Lambda girls are awful proud of having a member specializing now at Leland Stanford, but my, Rebecca Isaacstein has been at Bryn Mawr now four years."

LAVENDER: "Was Rebecca Isaacstein a Gamma girl? I have heard of her often and often."

PSYCLONIA: "Yes, and a daisy, too." *(Insinuatingly)* "What would you say, Lavender, to being a sister to her? I declare I am quite pining to call you 'sister' myself. Would you join, if I should work Our Girls for an invitation for you?"

LAVENDER: "I would have to write to my parents first, but I should think it would be perfectly lovely."

PSYCLONIA and GLADYS *(embracing her)*: "O do join, do! We could have the initiation at Calypso's house next Saturday. You could take the first degree then anyway!"

PSYCLONIA: "Great Scott, but we'll put her through. Why, when we initiated Circe O'Rourke, we suspended her from the third story of Rebecca Isaacstein's house and fed her on pepper and salt, and just—"

The Registrar appears.

Exeunt Omnes.

Hesperian, XXII:8, Feb. 15, 1893, pp. 3–5

A SENTIMENTAL THANKSGIVING DINNER

IN FIVE COURSES

"Ah, give me love and a feast like this,
  And in mine own countree,
And the gods may sit on their little thrones
  And nod, for all o' me.

CHORUS.

The world's still turn,
And the stars still burn,
And the gods are out on a spree,
They may have the rest
If they give me the best,
My love and mine own countree."
  —The Banqueter.

(A Fashionable Dining Room in Rome, the guests seated at table; at one end a crowd of two, much interested in conversation.)

COURSE ONE.

Consomme de Volaille a la Rosalie.

HE—"I cannot express my admiration for your tact in planning this dinner, Miss Ross."

SHE—"O! indeed I had nothing at all to do with it, Mr. Thornton, it was all mamma's doing; I should never have thought of it."

HE—"Let us grant, for argument's sake, that it is your mother who is the author and founder of the feast. It is none the less the most generous idea that has entered the brain of an American exile for decades. A New England Thanksgiving dinner in Rome! Why, it is equal to hearing 'Marching Through Georgia' on the Bosphorus. But I cannot comprehend how you ever accomplished such a delicate task here in this wilderness, for I know that the regulations which control the preparation of Thanksgiving dinner are as stringent as the laws of Draco, and as changeless as those of the Medes and Persians."

SHE—"It was not an easy task. Poor mamma's courage almost failed her once. Everything was so discouraging. Luccio, our cook, wept and tore his hair when we gave him the order for dinner. He declared that he would not prepare such dishes, that his reputation and the digestion of the guests would be ruined if he did. See, how pityingly Jacopo looks at us now. An hour ago he tasted the pumpkin pie, then shuddered and was still. And the worry those pies cost us! Mamma said she thought a dish of Nightingale's tongues could have been more easily procured."

(The servants bring on the next course.)

SECOND COURSE.

Quartier d'Agneau—Sauce Mousseline
Pommes Duchesses,
Jambon Westphalia a l'Anglaise.

HE—"What! will there be pumpkin pies? Even those? I wonder how many years have passed since I have eaten any? How fortunate you were to secure a Boston minister and have the traditional New England blessing."

SHE—"Yes. I don't think there are any real ministers on the Continent, no, nor in England. Of course there are rectors and clergymen, and D.D.'s, but no real ministers. We wanted the dinner to be as American as possible, for Thanksgiving day is so distinctly American. Next to the Fourth of July it seems more our own gala day than other."

HE—"You *are* an American, aren't you?"

SHE—*with surprise*—"Why, yes, we come from Maine, you know."

HE, *smiling*—"I had reference not so much to your American birth, as to your decided American sentiments. You are not a Cosmopolitan?"

SHE, *lowering her eyes*—"No. I think no American can be."

HE—"Most of your country women think differently."

SHE—"I know it, and I am sorry for it. But tell me, why does Miss Kelley wear glasses now, is it because she has such a nice nose for them?"

HE—"No, it is from over study, I believe. You see, she has had rather a trying year of it. I took her through the Borghese last week and learned all the particulars. This very confidentially, of course. In the first place, being a young woman of intellect, she wished to amply prepare herself for her tour. So last winter in Chicago she devoted herself to a course of reading. She informed me that she read an entire set of Ruskin, a large number of historical novels, many works on the flora and fauna of Europe, Abbot's 'Life of Napoleon,' Gibbon's 'Decline and Fall,' and somebody on the formation of the Alps."

SHE, *sympathetically*—"Poor thing."

HE—"Nor is that the worst of it! She commits to memory the name of the painter of every picture she sees, and the date of his birth and death. She went about among those bronze brethren in the Borghese muttering like a prophetess of Apollo. More than all this, she has a diary which takes a great deal of her time. I gleaned that it was a sort of running comment on art, poetry, history, religion, politics, philosophy and science, both ancient and modern. She has already completed five *duo decimo* volumes, which she has sent to her friends in Chicago. She hopes to be able to complete the entire series, unless, as her physicians fear, she breaks down from overwork."

SHE—"Oh, dear! Aren't that kind horrid? The kind that go about with note books and sketch books, and gather violets from Shelley's grave!"

HE—"They are hard to endure, and yet they are amusing."

SHE—"O, yes! I knew a party of young ladies from a college in Kansas who went abroad with their instructor in ornamental penmanship to study art. At the end of three months, one member of the party was near-sighted from her close application to her guide book, and another, the most promising student of the college, was ill with brain fever. During her delirium she repeated whole pages of Baedeker, and she died in Florence, gasping snatches of Roger's 'Italy' with her last breath."

(The servants enter and place the next course.)

THIRD COURSE.

Jeun Dindon—Sauce de Cranbaies
Pommes Parisiennes—Petits Pois.
Poulette de Printemps—au Cresson.

HE—"You are jesting now, but you spoke earnestly awhile ago."

SHE—"Yes."

HE—"Speak so again."

SHE, *reluctantly*—"I could speak more freely to you if you had not been in Italy for eight years. We have been laughing at the would-be intellectual American tourists. But there is a worse class still. I mean the class who really have talents and possibilities, who come abroad not to study, but, ostensibly to kill time, really to kill their nationality. They drift from Paris to Rome and from Rome to Baden, and spend their time in forgetting their Americanisms. I think the few gifted and brilliant men who leave America every year do it more harm than all the thousands of ignorant and debased Europeans who flock into Castle Garden. This living on the continent is becoming a dissipation among young Americans. It makes me heartsick to see American artists trying to become 'citizens of the world,' when every great work of art must be intensely national. There never was a cosmopolitan school of art, and never will be. This life of voluntary skill is especially weakening to Americans. The German artist may live in Paris, and the Parisian in Naples and yet not suffer much, for these continental nations are all bound together by ties of blood and by their common weakness. But we are away from all this conventionality, and cynicism, and agedness, and dwarfedness, and Ruins-of-empire, or ought to be, separated from it by three thousand miles of blue sea. Our world was fresh from God's fingers when this Europe was rotten to its core. We have the world's youngest born over there, and woe to us if we poison its youth."

HE—"But we must come in contact with the worst types of these nations in America, even."

SHE—"I do not think that the foreigners who come in at our ports can ever hurt us. It is only when we go abroad and take the venom into our own veins that we weaken our world over there, that is so completely cut off from this custom–ridden, priest–ridden, king–ridden Europe, and is touched only by the sea and sky, God's boundaries. Don't think I mean to preach, but it seems this way to me."

HE—"My own life must seem very aimless and futile to you. Well, it does to me. You do not think the great American novel will be written abroad?"

SHE, *firmly*—"No, I do not."

HE—"You are right enough."

SHE, *earnestly*—"I believe I am; I believe it with all my heart, and when I see the old cliffs of mine own country next month, I shall believe it still more."

HE, *starting visibly*—"What, you go so soon? I did not know."

(Enter servants with the next course.)

FOURTH COURSE.

Salade de Homard. Salade de Poulet.
Charlotte Russe a la Chantilly.

(He sits staring at his plate.)

SHE, *laughing*—"Does the news affect you so deeply?

HE, *quietly*—"I was wondering what there would be left in Tuscany after next month."

SHE, *blushing*—"Ah, indeed! Thanks, but that was too terribly forced."

HE, *inexpressibly*—"No, I don't mean it in that way, you know I don't, you must know it, your very consciousness must tell you. If it does not, then it is all useless, and I am a mistake, was borne one, and will die one. It is terrible of me to speak here in a crowd, but I have tried to tell you alone and could not. Your presence, unrelieved by that of others, always awes me. I can better

105

bear to tell you when these others are laughing around us, and, *(glancing at her face),* if the worst comes can bear it better."

HE, *after a long silence*—"You won't answer me?"

SHE, *her face whiter*—"Don't ask me, please. You see I have known it and felt it and lived so that it seems so strange to just *say* it now."

HE, *grasping a celery stalk with a hand that trembles*— "Do you mean that, Nell?"

SHE—"It seems to me, Gerald, that it is about the only thing I ever really meant in all my life, and as though no one else ever meant anything quite so really."

HE, *drinks a glass of ice water slowly before he can trust himself to speak*—"There is so much to tell you. Do you know the first—"

SHE—"But you must not tell me here, dear. You may just tell that one, though, if you will."

HE—"It was about that first night I saw you at the Harrises. I had lived here so long that I had almost forgotten that I was an American, and I was glad of it. Now and then I met American women who drifted into Rome, but they were all one of two kinds, either they had studied art in Paris and were 'doing' Italy, talked incessantly of art and impressionists and Corot and Bouguereau, and were so pedantic that they were unbearable, or they were 'citizens of the world,' who spoke French altogether, bought up old cameos, talked English politics, and delight in having a rather doubtful past, and present, for that matter. I had forgotten that there was any other type of American women. Then I met you that night, and you brought it all back, all that I had forgotten. I remembered all the things I used to be proud of when I was a boy, Bunker Hill Monument, and the Old North Church, and the historic elm, and the College, and someway, I was proud of them again. The next day I kept wanting to write odes to America and do other equally absurd things. Well, it went on and on until I met you that night at Prince Masellini's. You were all in white, with those red maple leaves sent you from the Adirondacks in your hair. Your hair and eyes are about the same color, you know, and when you are excited, they flash together, like the golden glory of a sunrise. That night you gave me three dances, and as your eyes laughed up through their depths of sun-dawn into mine, it seemed to me that you had all the glorious wealth of our Indian summer locked up in them, with the mists floating about you."

SHE, *desperately*—"Oh, please don't, *please*. I am blushing frightfully, and mamma is looking so shocked. I don't want my face to be red if my hair and eyes *are*."

HE—"Why, you are blushing, and for me! I must have you to myself a moment. It's terrible that it all came about here where these people are."

SHE, *laughing shyly*—"I am hardly responsible for how it came about, you know."

(Enter servants for the last time.)

FIFTH COURSE.

Gateaux Assortis. Confitures. Baisers de
Boston. Tarte a la citronille.
Oranges. Noix. Cafe Noir.

HE—"May we eat no more pies until we eat such as these in our own land."

SHE, *delightedly*—"Then you are going home?"

HE—"Do you think I could stand calmly and see the Atlantic grow between us?"

SHE—"I am so glad, so glad."

HE—"It will be about Christmas time when we get home. The first light snow will be falling, and the news-boys will be blowing their fingers and howling through the square. Chestnuts will be roasting on every corner, the shops will be gay with greens, and the bells will be crashing away in their windy steeples, and the very air will smell of Christmas. It will be good to be at home. At last! Your mother is getting ready to rise. You will go with me onto the terrace? I must see you alone. There will be star–lit nights on the Atlantic as we go over—"

SHE—"It will be rather cold on the deck, my dear."

HE, *as they rise*—"Well, never mind; there will be nights and nights, the stars will last forever, the stars and love."

SHE—"Signora Donati is frowning at you. She will call you to account tomorrow, and what will you say to her?"

HE, *grasping her hand rapturously behind the portiers* —"America for Americans."

Hesperian, XXII:4, Nov. 24, 1892, pp. 4–7

Poetry

SHAKESPEARE
A FRESHMAN THEME

World poet, we now of this latter day
Who have known failure and have felt defeat,
The dwarfed children of earth's sterile age,
Who feel our weakness weighing on our limbs
Unbreakable as bonds of adamant,
Turn to thee once again, O sun born bard:
To rest our weary souls a little space
Beneath the shadow of infinitude.
As weak men who have fallen very low,
Look toward high heaven and find some comfort there,
Knowing, however low themselves may fall,
The great blue reaches on, forever up.
O Mystery unsearchable! at times
We seek to find thy great soul's secret out,
And when some light streams like the setting sun
Across a watery waste, like swimmers bold

We plunge into that path of quivering gold,
And with long strokes we cleave the glowing wave
Straight toward the sun. But when its last caress
Leaves the horizon dark, about us steals
The awful horror of the open sea.
Thy mystery is great as is thy power,
And those who love thee most know only this,
As long since knew the men of Ithaca:
Within the great hall of our armory
Where hang the weapons of our ancient chiefs
And mighty men of old, there hangs a bow
Of clanging silver, which today no man,
Be he of mortal mother or the son
Of some sea goddess, can its tense drawn cord
Loosen, or bend at all its massive frame.
Beneath it hang the bronze shod shafts which none
Have cunning to in these days to fit thereto,
Above it all the sun stands still in heaven,
Pierced there long centuries with a shaft of song.

Hesperian, XXI:15, June 1, 1892, p. 3

ANACREON

The Muses found young Love one day,
  When mamma was not there,
They bound and carried him away
  To serve the Graces fair.
When Aphrodite found him gone,
  She thought him rather young,
And wrathfully she hastened on
  To free her captive son.
But when she cut the bonds of fate,
  Ah! sad the tale to tell,
The laddie's mamma came too late,
  He liked his job too well.

Sombrero, 1894, p. 222

110

COLUMBUS

O master of all seamen and all seas,
Who first dared set a sail toward sunset shores
Not as Odysseus sailed thou, for the love
Of blue sea water, nor of the sweet sound
Of surges smiting on thy vessel's prow;
Nor of the soft white bosom of thy sail
Swelling against blue heaven. Unto thee
The waters were but waste that lay between
Thee and thy prize. The stars of heaven, guides
That pointed toward the ever-widening west.
Prophet wert thou, who saw in things that were
Only the future, and thy soul was set
To journey toward the west, like kings of old
Who followed from the east a western star.
Most happy of all bards wert thou, who saw
Thy fancies take upon them form and shape
Thy realized ideal in the line
Of low, blue, coast that rose before thine eyes
At last, as it had done so oft in sleep,
In those low lengths of sunlit land that stretched
Into the smoking sunset. Thou whose soul
Saw what thine eyes, though fain, were weak to see;
Upon the swift wings of thy dreams, a world
Fast followed and thou didst create the west;
Even as He, the All-Begetting, once,
Sleeping his sleep of the eternities,
Was restless, stirred uneasily in space.
And into being dreamed the universe.

Hesperian, XXII:3, Nov. 1, 1892, p. 9

HORACE

BOOK I, ODE XXXVIII
PERSICOS ODI

"Boy, eastern luxury I hate,
Then cease my crown with flowers to plait,
Nor gather me the rose, that late
*   Withers, shrinking.*
For naught but simple wreaths I care,
With thee, my lad, to serve me there;
Under my shady myrtles fair,
*   Lightly drinking.*

Hesperian, XXII:4, Nov. 24, 1892, p. 12

Letters from
Willa Cather's Contemporaries

These letters, with the exception of those from W. W. Glass, are the results of an attempt made to obtain the recollections and impressions of all college classmates of Willa Cather. Many could not be located, some failed to reply, and a few gave me information which they asked me to withhold from publication. The letters included here are printed as they were written and without omissions, except for the names of the writers when requested.

Dear Sir: *Winchester, Va., Feb. 17, 1948*

Your letter of the 13th inst., addressed to the "Clerk of Frederick County," Winchester, Va., has been duly received by Mr. Lee N. Whitacre, Clerk, and referred to the undersigned for attention and reply, as the clerk and his staff find that their entire time is called for by the current business of the office, leaving them no time for historical or genealogical research.

The birth and death records of the period in question are in very bad condition, and a study of them calls for the utmost vigilance. These records are not indexed, and in many cases the names are not alphabetically arranged.

I have gone through these records with the utmost care, and I enclose herewith the results of my research. The birth record of "Willa Sibert Cather" (under that name) does not appear. I am inclined to the opinion that the birth record of "Jennie Cather" in 1881, may be the birth record of Willa Cather, and that she adopted the name "Willa" in later years.

I am in my 74th year, and I have been told that Chas. F. Cather pulled up stakes here when "Willa" was a mere infant, and removed to Red Cloud, Nebraska.

The records that I herewith enclose are all taken "verbatim" from the public records of the clerk's office of Frederick County, Va.

I expect to make further research in our public library, but in the meantime wish that you scrutinize these records very closely, and let me hear from you on the subject.

This research has required more than four hours intensive research. My minimum charge is at the rate of $1.00 per hour.

I examined the records between 1870 and 1877 with the utmost care, and find no birth that can possibly be construed as that of Willa Cather.

I am sending you this result of my research on the faith of your statement that you will make remittance therefor.

I am desirous of rendering you all assistance possible from this end of the line.

Very sincerely yours,
W. W. GLASS, Archivist,
Winchester, Virginia.

115

CLERK'S OFFICE OF FREDERICK COUNTY, VIRGINIA.
Marriage Register No. 1, p. 26 E. line 5. Cather, William M.
Smith, Emily A. C. Minister: Joseph Baker: Mar. 11, 1846.
Register of births Frederick County, 1853 forward. Aug. 5,
1864: Willela Cather, Female; Father Wm. Cather, Farmer;
Mother Emily C. Cather: No deformity; Reported by Wm.
Cather, Father.

Marriage Register No. 2, Page 181. Marriage of Charles F. Cather
to Jennie Boak, Dec. 5, 1872. (See copy from Register hereto
attached, and note that Charles F. Cather was a son of William
and Emily C. Cather, whose marriage is noted above. Note
also resemblance of the name "Willa" to that of her aunt
"Willela" above).

Register of Births of Frederick County, Va. 1870 to 1896. "June
24, 1877, Cather, Roscoe Boak (White; Male; Alive); Place
of Birth: Willow Shade; Father, Chas. F. Cather, Farmer, Residence; Willow Shade; Mother, Jennie B. Cather; Single birth;
No deformity; Information given by father." (This is found
in the "Northern District" of Frederick County, R. B. Smith,
Commissioner, Year Ending Dec. 31, 1877. The book is not
paged.)

Register of Births of Frederick County, Va., 1870 to 1896. "June
24, 1880, Cather, Julius, white, male, alive; Place of birth, N.W.
Grade (Meaning "Northwestern Turnpike" which passes
through what was formerly called the "Northern District" now
known as "Back Creek Dist.") Father, Chas. F. Cather, farmer,
residence N. W. Grade; Mother, Cather, Jane B. (single birth);
no deformity; information given by father, Chas. T. Cather.
(Book is not paged.)

Register of Births of Frederick County, Va., 1870 to 1896. "Aug.
27, 1881, Jennie Cather, white, female alive; Place of birth
N. W. Grade; Father Charles *C.* Cather, farmer; Residence
N. W. Grade; Mother Jennie B. Cather, single birth, no de-
formity; information given by Chas. C. Cather, Father. (Note:
The middle initial *"C"* must have resulted from the error of
the scrivener, as all other circumstances point to Chas. F.
Cather.)   Winchester, Va., Feb. 18, 1948.

I hereby certify the above extracts to be true copies from the original records of Frederick County Clerk's Office, Winchester, Va.

Given under my hand this 18th day of February, 1948.

W. W. GLASS, Archivist,
Winchester, Va.

FULL NAME OF HUSBAND	Charles F. Cather		
FULL NAME OF WIFE	Jennie Boak		
DATE OF MARRIAGE	December 5, 1872	PLACE OF MARRIAGE	Back Creek Valley, Va.

GROOM		BRIDE	
AGE: 24 years — mos. — days.		AGE: 22 years — mos. — days	
SINGLE OR WIDOWER	Single	SINGLE OR WIDOW	Single
BIRTHPLACE Frederick County, Va.		BIRTHPLACE Washington, D. C.	
RESIDENCE do	do	RESIDENCE Frederick County, Va.	
NAMES OF PARENTS William & Emily C. Cather		NAMES OF PARENTS William & Elizabeth Boak	
OCCUPATION Farmer			

MARRIED BY Rev. Edward J. Willis

A true copy. W. W. GLASS, Archivist.

Dear Sir: In re: Date of birth of Willa Sibert Cather.

I had an interview yesterday evening with Mrs. Marvin Larrick (nee Katie Andrews), at the nursing home of Miss May H. Heist, No. 511 Fairmont Ave., Winchester, Va., relative to the above matter.

Mrs. Larrick tells me that she herself was born on the N. W. Grade, near Hayfield, Frederick County, Va., in the year 1871; that she is a first cousin of Willa Sibert Cather, her mother having been Sarah Ellen Boak, only sister of Jennie Boak (Willa Cather's mother):

That Willa Cather was the eldest child of Chas. F. and Jennie Boak Cather; that Willa Cather was about three years younger than deponent; that three additional children were born in Frederick County to Chas. F. and Jennie Boak Cather, viz: Roscoe Boak Cather, Douglas (Julius) Cather, and Jessica (Jennie) Cather; that the family of William Cather and that of Chas. F. (his son) departed by wagon from Frederick County for the west while "Jessica" was a babe in arms; that at least one additional child (a son named "Jack") was born to Chas. F. Cather and wife after their arrival in the west:

That "Willow Shade" is identified as a large brick house still standing on the right hand side of the N. W. Grade about 200 or 300 yards south of "Back Creek";

That deponent's aunt "Jennie Cather" taught school in the village now known as "Gore," 13 miles N. W. of Winchester; that deponent and her cousin Willa Cather attended school at Mr. Smith's school in Gore; that deponent was eleven years old when the Cathers set out for the west, and that she was one of the gathering that saw them depart:

That the "Boak" family removed from Washington, D. C. to Gore, and their dwelling house is still standing, and was known as "The Cedars."

That Willa Cather was of exceptional mentality even when a young girl, before school age, and that she delighted to stand on the foot bridge which leads across the stream from the road to "Willow Shade" and recite the poem "I stood on the bridge at midnight, while the clock was striking the hour etc."

Mrs. Larrick is very frail physically, was in bed when interviewed, but her mind seemed as clear as a bell, and her recollection did not seem to falter at any time.

I have again checked the register of births, but am forced to the conclusion that the birth of Willa Cather is lacking by reason of oversight on the part of her parents in the matter of reporting it.

Who's Who gives Willa Cather's birth date as Dec. 7, 1876. The evidence points clearly to an earlier date, probably 1874.

I still have prospects of obtaining further information, which I will send you in due course.

Yours etc.
W. W. GLASS, Archivist.

Santa Monica, California,
March 15, 1948

Dear Mr. Shively:

Regret that cannot remember any particular incidents re Miss Cather that would be of interest. Do recall seeing her at Theatre down town when stage plays stopped on cross country tours. I had several classes in Eng. Lit. department, under Sherman, Louise Pound, also course in Shakespeare. Did Daily Themes, presume Miss Cather must have been in some of these classes, but not sure. Of course often spoke to others later how proud the Class of '95 must be to have had such a member. With Chancellor Canfield, Gen. Pershing there also was more that could be commented on. I enjoyed reading her novels. One winter when in Honolulu found most of them, which showed their general popularity and read some had missed.

My remembered impression is that Miss Cather was energetic, independent, and capable.

Wish could give you something worth while.

Sincerely,
A. N. MOODY

> *Denver, Colorado*
> *Feb. 27, 1948*

Dear Mr. Shively:

I am very sorry to be tardy in replying to your letter in re Willa Cather, but it could not be helped.

I knew Willa Cather slightly personally. Indeed, I think no one knew her well — except the sisters — the Pounds. She was brilliant and, really, queer, as she associated so very little with any one else. I knew her by reputation and to say little more than "Good Morning" or similar greetings.

She was very egotistical: really had the right to be! One never could think of her as a friend. I've been told that she was more cordial in later years.

Miss Cather always gave some of us the feeling that she regarded herself as *far above us*—but that did not bother us at all.

I've enjoyed some of her books even tho she was always before me while reading. I have never considered her a friend, a real one, to any one! She was *not* a good dresser while in school and one always knew that she felt superior—which often amused us. From what I've heard I think she was more kindly, perhaps, in later years; but she was always "superior." That was her attitude.

I have read very little which she has written. Have had no inclination to do so. Please do *not* "credit" me!

> Very truly,
> Yours for U. of N. always.
> (Name withheld by request) 1894

> *Renton, Wash.*
> *February 29, 1948*

Dear Mr. Shively:

In response to your letter of the 23rd, I will say that I have very little to give you in connection with Miss Willa Cather.

She was a member of my class 1895. I entered the University in the fall of 1888, the Preparatory class. I have the impression that the first impression that I had of Willa Cather was as Captain of the Ladies Cadet Company. I watched the Company drill on several occasions.

She wore the costume of the Co. Had a sword buckled around her and marched with dignity and precision as a commanding officer.

Do not recall that I was in any of her classes. She was member of the Union Literary Society. Traveled around with the group that belonged there.

You might get more information from Clark Oberlies now living in Tacoma, Washington.

Charles Weldon living in Pasadena, Cal. might be able to add to your information.

He is said to be the character in one of her earlier books.

Truly,
W. H. H. FORSYTH

James R. Shively, Sir:

This letter arrived some time ago. Sorry but I cannot recall anything that would be of interest about Willa Cather that others could not have told you. While I was in the Uni. during all her U. of N. career I was never in any of her classes. My sister was in her French class under Miss Conklin. Her report was that she was not the most outstanding pupil but among the best in the class.

I was a member of the "Union" Society as was Miss Cather. She always did her part on any program. I do not remember any unusual part—but *think* she was a debater once.

She was a very mild exponent of the modern miss as to dress. But while comfort and less fuss was her idea she was always very *neat* in her dress—a mannish hat—well cut coat and vest was her great pride when Feminine clothes were fussy and cartwheel sized hats covered Gibson Like hair dresses. Our "shirtwaists" (not blouses then) were quite well ornamented also. Sorry to have taken so much time to reply but hoped I could think of some particular item of interest. She was not much of a mixer but 2 of her friends were mine also.

Yours sincerely,
(Name withheld by request.)

121

In re: Willa Cather.

Dear Mr. Shively:

When the two–year preparatory course was given at the university in 1890 Willa Cather came into the school and we preps eventually became the class of '95.

Almost exact opposites in every way we became good friends. We had double seats or desks on the top floor of the old Hall in brusque old Dr. Hunt's English class, and we were seatmates.

We were not allowed the back seat we had chosen, very long, for I drew pictures—sketches to make her laugh, and she wrote more or less villainous blank verse in return, so Dr. Hunt insisted we occupy the very front desks. I was only fifteen.

Willa was just plain Billy to all of us. She wore very mannish clothes—high stiff collars with string tie or four–in–hand–mannish white cuffs peeping out the plain suit coat she always affected. I never remember her wearing a dress at any time. Always dark man-tailored suits.

She was not a shrinking violet even at 17 but bright–eyed—alert and rather assertive.

One Monday having given no time to preparing the required theme because of a week end trip she said, "Watch me tangle up the argumentative old Doc, till he forgets to ask for our papers." The discussion sounded innocent enough and involved partly a disputed point between them as to whether the eyes alone gave expression to the face. Before she argued the birds off the bushes, the 40 minute period was over and class dismissed. She won. He forget the themes. Many were the heated discussions between them on strategy in story writing.

She wrote shorts for the *Nebraskan* and *Sombrero* '95 has a football story with Dorothy Canfield writing with her.

Logarithms and cosecants were no part of her daily round and she took only a scant amount of Greek and Latin as I remember. Since I had 5 years of each our paths diverged. At graduation time while I played Antigone and took part in the Greek Chorus she helped edit the *Sombrero* for that year which was no small job.

Once after graduation when she returned for Alumni Day, she

told me she was reading mss. on an eastern magazine of note and had the chance to turn down mss. by Kipling. She regarded that as a huge joke. Her work as a literary critic on eastern magazines has been well written up by the *Journal* and University people upon several occasions.

She was an unique figure aside from her mannish dress. Scarcely medium height. She spoke in a more or less monotone best suited to scanning verse. Never a favorite with the boys because she was so mannish herself. They dutifully dated her once and then were scared off. A mature mind in a young woman of 17 is unusual and no doubt she knew even then what she planned to do.

Writing blank verse all thru English class was a favorite diversion rather than listening unless she could start an argument. Painstaking with all her work, she was neat and accurate but not enthusiastic except it were her hobby, English.

I doubt if the little I can tell you of her early days will be of any help at all to you and you need have no concern to mention me in your paper for my name would mean nothing after all these years.

I stayed on in Lincoln teaching and nearly finished my master's degree. I did not write my thesis. I was offered a scholarship in Philosophy and Eng. Lit. to Cornell but did not accept for I came to Kansas City and soon lost contact with Billy Cather.

She had considerable talent acting in amateur theatricals and invariably wore men's clothing. Her hair was close cropped and generally with a very stubby pompadour. She did not like girls' ways or manners. She drifted into a friendship with me mostly because of our completely opposite traits. She played a fair game of tennis and that with vigor but not too much interest.

Good luck on your thesis. You have a good subject. When I get around to it I shall write the "Great American novel" and claim my M.A. It would be better for the world at large if they'd give my degree to me to keep me from writing.

Very sincerely

Kansas City, Mo.　　　　　　GRACE MORGAN RILEY
Feb. 27–48.

March 1, 1948

My dear Mr. Shively:

It was my good fortune to be a member of the Class of 1895 at the University of Nebraska, the class to which Miss Willa Cather belonged. As you have already learned, Willa Cather was a distinctive individual. My chief recollections are of an energetic young woman wearing sober, mannish–cut dresses. I always see her in a straw hat of "flattish" design.

In the early 90's the Nebraska Campus was a democratic place. However, some of us were compelled to consecrate ourselves to the business of living as well as learning. Consequently we may not have come to know as well as we might, those more fortunate students like Willa Cather, who had the benefit of time to give to extra–curricular matters. As the record shows, she was intensely interested in the student papers. I hope these are available to you. Some twenty years ago I gave to the University Library some bound volumes of the student papers. Therein should be considerable material tracing back to Willa Cather.

I am sorry I cannot be more precise and photographic.

Very sincerely yours,

ECE:gs　　　　　　　　　　EDWARD C. ELLIOTT

Minneapolis, Minn.
March 2, 1948

Dear Mr. Shively:

In reply to your letter of February 23, will say that I remember Willa Cather very well. She was always at the top in her classes, especially ones pertaining to English and Literature in general.

She was always courteous and affable and made me feel at ease in her presence.

I recall that she was somewhat inclined to adopt mannish styles in her dress and she was the first girl that I ever saw in "suspenders." I presume they were merely pieces of cloth crossed over her waist and attached to her belt, but the "effect" is what I remember.

Yours very truly,

JBB:d　　　　　　　　　　JESSE B. BECHER

Grain Exchange　　　　　　1894 and 1896

124

March 2nd, 1948

Dear Mr. Shively:

I have yours of February 23rd but there is probably very little information which I can give which you do not already have. Willa Cather was of the Class of '96 and I was in Class of '94 but I probably knew her better than many in my own class. She was a member of the Union Society of which I was a member until my senior year. I also used to see her in connection with our work on the *Hesperian,* the college publication. She was perhaps editor for sometime, at least contributed largely and I at that time was looking after the physical make-up of the *Hesperian* and also was part owner of the little stationery shop in the basement of the main building, which was the *Hesperian* office.

Willa was an individualist. She often wore a starched shirtwaist and a comparatively short skirt, both of which were somewhat uncommon in those days. Although boyish in her dress and at times in her mannerism, she was never even inclined towards coarseness. She was not the feminine type that cared for lace and feminine finery.

I gave no thought at that time as to her future but as she developed as an author, it was not in the least surprising to me. She had shown promise in that field although I never appreciated at that time the extent of her ultimate goal.

I doubt if she had as many friends even among the girls as the average co-ed. Dorothy Canfield Fisher was, in effect, a protegé of Willa's, and they were often together due probably to their mutual instincts as later developed in the lives of both of them. I do not remember of any "boy friend" that Willa had. Co-eds in those days did not drink or smoke—or even pet in public but, it would not be natural to think of Willa as drinking, smoking or petting. She probably was as close personally to Louise and Olivia Pound who, I think, could give you more information about her than any of her group now left in Lincoln.

Willa was always quite out-spoken but never to the extreme and never unfairly. She was a girl that I very much liked and

125

respected but I would hardy say that she was a girl that I was fond of, if you get the minor distinction.

The word that I earlier used "individualist" is a characterization that should not be omitted.

What I have given you above will be of little help but in any case remember that I prefer not to have my name mentioned. It would have no place in a thesis such as you apparently have in mind. If there are any detailed questions that you want to ask me, I will make a try at answering them.

Good luck to you.

Very truly yours,
(Name withheld by request.)

Yes, Mr. Shively:

I was a student in Nebraska State Univ. when Willa Cather attended. However I worked when I was not attending classes, in the University Library. So, you see, I had practically no time to mingle with the students. I knew Willa Cather in a general way, that she was a promising person and had literary gifts and I always felt that Dr. Sherman was aware of her literary bent and was interested in her from that standpoint.

All this is too general to be of any interest to you, I am sure, and I regret that I cannot be of more help. I might add that her mannish style of dress did not appeal to me, but of course that is purely personal taste and of no consequence.

Sincerely,
FLORENCE S. SMITH

Lincoln, Nebr.
March 4th, 1948

Mr. James R. Shively:

I do not care to put my personality into your thesis, but that you may catch the pitch of my mind and judge the value of the literary tones I caught at the University of Nebr. last century, I will introduce some personal matters. I came, a very poor farm lad to Lincoln in 1889. I fought my way by way of Lincoln High School to matriculation at the university as a freshman in the fall of 1892. My future plans were rather hazy but I wanted to drink rather deeply at the springs of Literature on the classic level. I took many courses in Latin, Greek, German and a little French in undergraduate days. English was my favorite, however, and in that I majored for graduate study. I was forced to stay out of school one year to earn money to pay my way. In order to graduate with my entrance class in 1896 it was necessary to load my study schedules very heavily. This, together with my lack of money shut me off from many social contacts I would gladly have made, and prevented me from developing others entered into. In those days the "barb–frat" fight among students was something very real, with the majority siding with the "barbs." These found social expression in the Delian, Palladian and Union literary societies. There was another society whose name at this moment I do not readily recall. As for me I became a Palladian and was not so well acquainted with Miss Cather who was a Union. In that club she was tied in with such people as Olivia and Louise Pound, Hartley Burr Alexander, Ned and Luther Abbott, Evalina Rolofson, Harvey Newbranch and several others becoming more or less notable in their graduate life. There was a slightly radical tone, something after the populist democrat political spirit of the time, stirring amongst most of the group—just enough to give exhileration to their spirits. Any of these should be able to help you. Besides these were the Westermann boys among the fraternity boys, Miss Dorothy Canfield (now Mrs. Fisher), Professor Adams and Herbert Bates of the English Department. Will Owen Jones, *State Journal* Editor, was known to the group also.

Miss Cather was higher class woman when I entered the university and was pretty much of a fixture in the group noted above. These, together with certain students from the other literary societies were publishers of a certain college monthly whose name I do not now recall, besides the *Hesperian,* the Weekly *Nebraskan* (which soon after became the *Daily Nebraskan*). The latter seems to have been published more or less of a private enterprise but had fraternity support. Among the young people it was called "Riley's Rag" after young Riley who got it out. There was also a quarterly literary magazine sponsored by the English department and intended to invite a better grade of formal writing. I do not remember its exact name but it only lived two or three years. The University Library should be able to help you to copies of this material and also the university annuals then published under the name of *Sombrero.* If you cannot find them there try the State Historical Society. I well remember Miss Cather's stuff in some of the publications mentioned. Besides this she was connected with the editorial department of the *State Journal.*

You ask as to my impressions of Miss Cather's personality. Well, she was a stockily-built young lady of medium height. Her face was not one of doll–like beauty, but was strong and good to look at, brunette but rather light. Her voice was somewhat low-pitched, at least alto, and her hearty laugh was rich and reminded you of nutty flavors. She wore bobbed hair and as I remember combed it somewhat pompadour. Also her skirts were not sidewalk length. These last two items, in that day, impressed other women as somewhat daring. Oh yes, she wore white hard-starched shirt fronts and what people called linked cuffs sometimes. Her conversation was forceful.

They say you may know people by their friends. Well, that Will Westermann, one of the university's most cultured scholars together with the family of Chancellor Canfield and his highly gifted daughter (Mrs. Dorothy Canfield Fisher) were her prized friends speaks volumes along that line. From names mentioned above and publications, which the university library and that of the historical society should be able to make available I hope you may glean much. Also you should be able to get through these libraries' lists of her publications.

Because I learned the dire difficulties in the way of digging up material, much of it vanished or unavailable, for a master's thesis, I have been glad to try to extend a little help. However, you must remember that the mould of trouble and the rusts of time have been gnawing away at materials stored away in my mind over a half of century ago and left undisturbed since. Many memories of that day have doubtless faded and some disappeared or become sadly warped.

Yours in friendship,
JASPER HUNT

Jotted down hastily on
a busy afternoon.

March 26, 1948

Dear Mr. Shively:

I am convalescing following an accident early in February and so have been unable to answer your letter promptly.

I remember Willa Cather very well although I had only a speaking acquaintance. Her literary aptitude was recognized around the university then. I'm not sure but it seems to me she did some work on the *State Journal*. She was not fastidious in her dress. She was friendly, had a cheerful grin usually and I have the impression she had her objectives pretty clearly in mind and was down to business going after them.

I wish I could give you some more clear recollections; but these remain after the years.

Sincerely,
OTIS G. WHIPPLE

Pasadena 4, California
March 5, 1948

Dear Mr. Shively:

Yes, I well remember Willa Cather on the Campus of Our Alma Mater, Uni. of Nebraska, as she strode the walks in her dignified, business-like manner. She always seemed to know what she wanted and earnestly went after her quest—which was writing.

We occasionally met, especially on the way to the Nebraska Hall where Dr. Bessey, Dr. Ward's Offices and Laboratories were; or on the walk toward the Library, or downtown past the Chemistry building.

I do not remember any particular incident affecting our student life, however, I do remember my respect for her sincerity in the field of her interest in Literary Work, far removed from my interests in the Sciences, particularly Chemistry. She was apparently engaged in exploring the surface of the Earth, the various inhabitants thereof, in other words—people and their visible surroundings. Willa Cather seemed to be making an effort to reach the highest literary attainments and surmount them if possible, while I, Mary Louise Fossler, was primarily interested in the Causes in Life, striving to better understand the living Unit—the Cell, the fundamental spark of life and its development to the highest form of Life, while she was interested apparently in the highest form of life, humanity, and its environments.

Dr. Fling had taught us the Sources Method in History, which impressed me very much. Dr. Bessey, and Dr. Ward taught us morphology and Prof. Nicholson taught us concerning atoms and Molecules. Willa Cather and I apparently were trying to explore the World from opposite directions.

I well remember her Irish blue eyes and dark hair and her Anglo—or rather her superior air. I graduated in 1894 and she graduated in 1895. She received Literary Honors, I received my M.A. and Sigma Xi Honors in 1898.

I have never been sorry to have chosen Chemistry for my Major interest. The atoms and molecules have never lied to me nor have they ever shown partiality or class distinction, while the Human relationships have been filled with deceptions, which I fail to appreciate.

Sincerely

Signed MARY LOUISE FOSSLER

March 9, 1948

Dear Mr. Shively:

Your letter of inquiry in respect to my recollection of Miss Willa Cather has just been received.

In reply I am afraid that I cannot add much to the information you already have. It was either good fortune or the reverse to have been one of those who had to do work on the outside, to pay my expenses, while I was in attendance at the University and consequently I had to forego much of the social side of life while there. Hence my recollections are mostly objective.

Of course Miss Cather was one of the outstanding members of the Class of 1895, along with such personalities as Dorothy Canfield and Olivia Pound. But Miss Cather was a Maverick. She wore her hair cut short—was assertive and independent, in her actions and demeanor—hence became an outstanding personality on the campus.

I understand that she was in violent disagreement with Dr. Sherman, head of the English Department, in respect to his "Analytics of Literature," and did not hesitate to tell him so emphatically.

As I was not acquainted with her personally, I regret that I cannot give you any specific help on your thesis.

I am,

Yours very truly,

WARREN W. WOODS

131

March 3, 1948

Dear Mr. Shively:—Your letter of inquiry concerning knowledge pertaining to the history of Miss Willa Cather, U. of N., '95, as she appeared in undergraduate days, is addressed to my husband (name withheld by request). Since I entered the University simultaneously with Miss Cather, autumn '91, and was also rated a Freshman, as was she, and since we both attended the same division of Freshman Mathematics—Trigonometry and Conic Sections—taught by Prof. H. E. Hitchcock, and since we, two, both, were members of the Board of Editors of Vol. III of the *Sombrero* issued by the Class of '95, in the University's Quarter Centennial year, perhaps my contribution as to knowledge of her might be a bit more intimate. Evidently my husband thinks so, for he has referred your inquiry to me.

I hope you have a copy of *Sombrero,* Vol. IV, before you. To the make–up of the literary portion of that Annual, Miss Cather was rightly assigned the responsibility. You will note that on page 222 there appears a poem, "Anacreon," by "W.C." On page 224 begins the First Prize Story, and the authors given are "Willa Cather and Dorothy Canfield." On being asked how such a story could be written by two authors, Miss Cather replied: "Dorothy produced the plot. I did the writing."

You have asked in regard to Miss Cather's manner, appearance, scholastic and literary abilities, activities at the University, etc.

Miss Cather's greatest contribution to the life of the University was through the high quality of her literary labors. She contributed articles for publication in the two University papers— the older one, the *Hesperian,* and the later paper, the *Nebraskan.*

I knew Miss Cather best as I saw her five days a week in Freshman Mathematics, for two semesters. She wished to be considered "boy-like," dressing her hair as did the men students —"shingled" and parted on the side. She always dressed in "middies," blouses, accompanied by full skirts, freeing her from the restraints of clothes worn by young women of that day. In conversation, she affected the slang expressions used by the boys. She said that her name, Willa, was the feminine of William. Some of the students objected to some of the language she used in her First Prize Story, Vol. III, of the *Sombrero*. She was approached to make changes in the language, and, I think did so! She often voiced aloud, in the freedom of conversational time between classes, addressing a very small bevy of admiring students—1). non–belief in God; 2). that she could not learn Mathematics, and that she was not going to be cheated out of receiving a diploma for graduation due to failure in Mathematics!

(One day, Prof. Hitchcock detained several of her classmates in Mathematics, asking if they knew whether cheating was going on in that section of the Class. The reply was in the affirmative.)

After our Freshman year I had few intimate contacts with Miss Cather. When I became President of Class '95 in its senior year, she attended Class meetings, and her vocal contributions to those meetings were sensible suggestions, but strongly advocated. I never felt that she deserved the opprobrium of being called a "politician." The Class was proud to have her as a member, due to its recognition of her literary ability. It hardly loved her. Her circle of friends was small. They were of her own selection. Among them was Dorothy Canfield, much younger in years. Dorothy completed her 2nd Preparatory Year, summer '95, when her father, Chancellor J. H. Canfield, left the University.

Miss Cather was a member of Union Literary Society. I cannot recall that Miss Cather made any special contribution to the University through that Society. She was not a "mixer," nor was she an "all–round" student. I cannot recall that she took any part in Athletics. Her one outstanding quality was her literary genius.

I would prefer that you not quote me by name, please.

Have you seen the enclosed clippings? I am sorry they are not dated. The persons sending them to me, failed to register the date of her death. Sorry—but, you have that, anyhow! Kindly return.

Most cordially,

(Name withheld by request.)

(Why I graduated in '96, is because, largely that I came from a 3-yr. High School—Falls City, Nebr. When called a Freshman, of Class '95, I carried but one Freshman study—Mathematics. I took an extra semester after Class '95 had graduated, thus belonging to Class '96.)

March 2, 1948

My dear Mr. Shively:

I regret that this letter, in response to your request regarding information about Miss Cather, must be strongly negative. The situation is that I am on leave of absence for this semester with a definite commitment to finish a book on research by the fall of this year. For reasons of heavy teaching and other delays I am far behind schedule. Also, my memory of Miss Cather during the period she spent at Lincoln is not very clear any more.

You will find most of the material which I would know in her novel "One of Ours." The Erlich family, which is presented there, is my family. Her depiction of the dinners which "Claude" attended at the Erlich house contains memories of the many meals, on Sunday particularly, which Miss Cather took at our house with my Father and Mother and my five brothers, who in 1891–92, were all living in the house formerly occupied by Chancellor Canfield on "S" street. I wish I could be of help to you but I can not take the time now to assemble my memories.

With best wishes for the success of your study, I am,

Very sincerely yours,

WILLIAM LINN WESTERMANN

Dear Mr. Shively:

Your information is correct, I was in the University at the same time as "Billy" Cather, as we called her. I remember her very well. She took no part in the social activities of the school and had no beaus. She wore her hair cut short like a man's and was very mannish in her appearance and actions. If she were there today she would no doubt be wearing a man's clothes.

She thought very well of herself and even then fancied herself as a writer. She contributed a regular column to the *Daily Nebraskan* entitled "Pastels in Prose," in which she indulged in cruel, cynical, unjust and prejudiced criticism of everyone on the campus, both students and profs. I finally got fed up on this stuff to the extent that I wrote an article for the paper called "Postals in Paste" in which I took her apart, after which her contributions ceased.

Her first book, *O Pioneers* is about as poor and sophomoric a bit of writing as I have ever read. She did much better, from a literary standpoint, in her later books, but she has in all of them, especially in those written about the Midwest, her early home, been cynical, cruel, unjust and prejudiced, just as she was in the things she wrote for the school paper.

There was in the University at the same time as Billy Cather, another girl, who later became a very well known writer. This was Dorothy Canfield, daughter of the then chancellor. She was the exact opposite of Miss Cather, and enjoyed the affection and respect of everyone.

So far as I know Miss Cather had no friends and wanted none.

Yours truly,

E. C. AMES

Lincoln, March 31, 1948

My dear Mr. Shively:

I fear I have very little information that would be of use to you, as I had but slight personal acquaintance with Miss Cather.

She was not in my class and I am not sure that we were in any classes together.

You see at that time lower classmen were pretty much limited to required work in their chosen course.

However as the student body was small, she was a well known figure on the campus, largely because of her appearance.

Miss Cather wore her hair cut short—quite boyish—and favored blouses of the shirt type, dark wool ones in winter, long before the day of bobbed hair and the so-called shirtwaist. This gave her a rather masculine look.

You probably know that the young people are very critical and we were quite mid–Victorian in those years, 1890–on. So I believe we thought more about her oddness than her scholastic ability, about which most of us knew little. Naturally, she shone in English.

It was in her Freshman year that Dr. Canfield came to the Uni as Chancellor, and Miss C and Dorothy (Canfield Fisher) were good friends, seen often together. This no doubt was due to their budding literary talents as they presented a strange contrast.

Dorothy must have been a good bit younger and was very much the little girl while Willa seemed much more mature and as I said quite independent in her dress.

If you can sift anything usable from this, you are very welcome to use it in any way you like in your own words and without quotes or credit. If not, simply discard it.

Wishing you success in your thesis,

Sincerely,

(Name withheld by request)

Apr. 1, 1948

Dear Mr. Shively:

In reply to your letter of March 27, asking for my recollections of Miss Willa Cather, would say that I remember Miss Cather in a general way very well but I am afraid that I cannot give you any circumstances which might be of value to you since I was not intimately acquainted with her, was not in any classes with her that I can remember and had very little social contacts with her.

Needless to say, Miss Cather was an outstanding personality even in her student days. She was rather masculine in dress and demeanor without being coarse; was self-confident, positive, alert, vivacious, not at all coquettish.

I am sorry that I cannot give you any personal incidents or impressions of her, but 52 to 56 years is stretching the memory a little far. I am sure that you will have better luck with many who knew her better.

If she is still living I should be glad to learn where and how well.

With kindest regards and best wishes for the success of your thesis, I am

Yours very truly,

EDWARD Y. PORTER, '96.

April 2, 1948

Dear Mr. Shively:

In re: Willa Cather, Deceased

I have yours of March 27, 1948 and note what you say. I entered the University of Nebraska from the Lincoln High School in the fall of 1891. Chancellor Canfield, a great man, took over the University for the next four years. Willa entered the same year, or, perhaps, she may have come in from the preparatory school then maintained. We were classmates. After our graduation in the spring of 1895, I stayed on for two years and went through the law school and took a second degree in American History and English Literature.

During the season of 1894 and 1895 she was editor of the college paper, the *Hesperian*. I was her editorial writer. The next year I was editor of the paper and Harvey Newbranch was my editorial writer and we had a row with Chancellor McClean. That fact enables me to fix the date when Willa was editor. You can verify this if you can find the files of the *Hesperian*. As strange as it may seem, I haven't a single copy. Fifty years is a long time.

Miss Cather belonged to the Union Literary Society and I belonged to the Palladian Literary Society. We were good friends and sometimes studied French, or Latin, or German, or something of that kind in the Chapel, but my particular recollection of her is due to the years of association on the *Hesperian*. She was a very good student but not what one would call brilliant except in a literary way. She was ambitious to be a writer and surely went to the top. She had a very even disposition and was calm and quiet in her attitude but had very positive ideas. She told me once that she did not read the daily papers because she would obtain a distorted idea of events. We often discussed the editorials but she never turned any of them down.

She was a normal sized girl, about 5′ 6″ and weighed in the neighborhood of 120 lbs. Her features were even and I think her hair was brown. She was neither a blonde or a brunette. Her complexion was clear. She wore her hair short and in those days this was considered rather mannish by most people. Bob Ingersoll came to the University to lecture and the next morning she told me that Bob was a great poet and a favorite of hers. The only criticism I ever had from her was that she couldn't tell my "a's" from my "o's" and asked me if I couldn't make an "a."

If Willa ever had any boyfriends I never saw her with anybody. So far as I know she was not much interested in social life. I don't think she had any close girlfriends among the girls either. She was very fond of Professors Sherman and Wolfe. We often discussed Robert Browning, Henry James and Rudyard Kipling. The last two were just appearing over the horizon.

She and Dorothy Canfield, who was much younger than

Willa, wrote a football story that is published in the 1895 or 1897 annual. Willa was reserved and indifferent to ordinary people and consequently appeared to be rather lonely. She was not a snob however. She was bent on an intellectual career.

About 1899 Willa was connected with a paper in Pittsburgh and she wrote to me to see if I could send her a *Hesperian*. She wished it for some information. At that time she said that she was going with McClure's Magazine. I have all of her books, some of them I did not care for. I think that her best book and her best novel is "My Ántonia."

I hope I have been able to help you in your research. Credit is not necessary.

Yours very truly,
B. C. MATHEWS

BCM:dk

P.S. The students of the 90's have always been proud of the attainments of Willa Cather, Dorothy Canfield, General Pershing and Roscoe Pound.

B. C. M.

Hollywood 46, California,
March 21, 1948

Dear Mr. Shively:

Your letter of Feb. 23rd asking for my recollections of Miss Willa Cather, a classmate of mine at the University of Nebraska, came duly to hand.

Of course I remember her tho I did not have a close personal acquaintance with her, due largely to different scholastic and literary groupings. For example at that early date, when the differences between Fraternities and Non-fraternity student organizations were not so much emphasized, the non-fraternity group predominated. Representing this group in a social and literary way were two large open literary societies—The Palladian, and the Union between which there was a friendly rivalry. I was a Palladian, Miss Cather was a Union. Each society held weekly meetings each in their own halls in the Main University Building. These were held Friday evenings and it was an unwritten law that the young men should escort some member of the fair sex to the meetings. This worked fine through the use of the "slate." Thus social contacts were made and developed. Now, Miss Cather being a Union and I a Palladian we did not have this social contact and the added acquaintance that would have followed with it.

The year that our class was Juniors (1894) the University of Nebraska celebrated its Quarter–Centennial Anniversary. During these early years it was customary for each succeeding Junior class to issue a University publication known as the Junior Annual.

Our class assumed the task of its publication, selected an editorial board and named the forthcoming publication *Sombrero, '95, University of Nebraska."* C. R. Weldon and J. W. Searson were made editors–in–chief and were ably supported by eleven associate editors among whom was Miss Willa Cather.

It was decided at once to feature the Quarter–Centennial Anniversary celebration. As an associate editor Miss Cather showed ability, cooperation, industry and a genius for doing things and for getting others to do things.

Miss Cather, as I recall, was a good student particularly of English language and literature. Her prize Story "The Fear That Walks By Noonday" was published in the *Sombrero*. Those who knew her at this time were not surprised when later she became one of the foremost fiction writers of her day.

In your letter to me you ask for what I can recall of Miss Cather "her manner, appearance, scholastic and literary ability, activities at the university, information about material she wrote at that time, or anything else you may recall about her." Some of these things I have already given you.

Now as to her physical appearance, would say that it was not unlike that of the average run of girls. She was of medium height, perhaps slightly overweight, but in general her physical bearing was good and her body well developed.

I recall that in her Freshman year she wore her hair short and uncurled. Why I never knew. But with the feminine fashion of the day—shirt waists with white stiff collar and black tie—it gave to her something of a mannish appearance on first acquaintance. Her face was unusually alert and intelligent.

She came of a good cultured family and chose her friends of the cultured type, among them being Chancellor and Mrs. Canfield. The Chancellor's daughter, Dorothy, was associated in the authorship of the story referred to "The Fear That Walks By Noonday."

Very truly yours

CHARLES R. WELDON

April 23, 1948

Dear Mr. Shively:

I owe you a humble apology for leaving your letter of Febr. 23d on my desk so long without attention. I was (and still am) immersed in the work of revising my Textbook of Mycology, of which the first edition appeared in 1935. In this work I piled all sorts of books and pamphlets on my desk and your letter wormed its way underneath these, at least it remained hidden. Today my conscience pricks me so hard that I take this up first thing today.

Willa Cather was a couple of years ahead of me at the University but I knew her. She was a great friend of the Gere family, especially of the older daughter Mariel. From her you can doubtless obtain considerable information. Miss Cather used to write for University publications (student publications, I mean). The one that I remember best was a joint authorship story by her and Dorothy Canfield, appearing in the *Sombrero,* as the Junior class publication was then known. This was, I believe, the first published story of the younger author. These two were intimate friends for many years, but I have heard the rumor that this friendship broke up many years later. You can doubtless obtain information concerning Miss Cather by writing to Mrs. Dorothy Canfield Fisher, Arlington, Vermont.

Miss Cather was a very good student and a leader in literary work among the students. She held important places in the

141

student body. She was rather thick-set and never very handsome. She was rather positive in her opinions, but usually had a good basis for these.

I wonder if you are any relative of Amy Shively, who was a year or so behind me at the University. I knew her rather well.

Very truly yours

ERNEST A. BESSEY
U. of N. '96
Professor of Botany, retired.

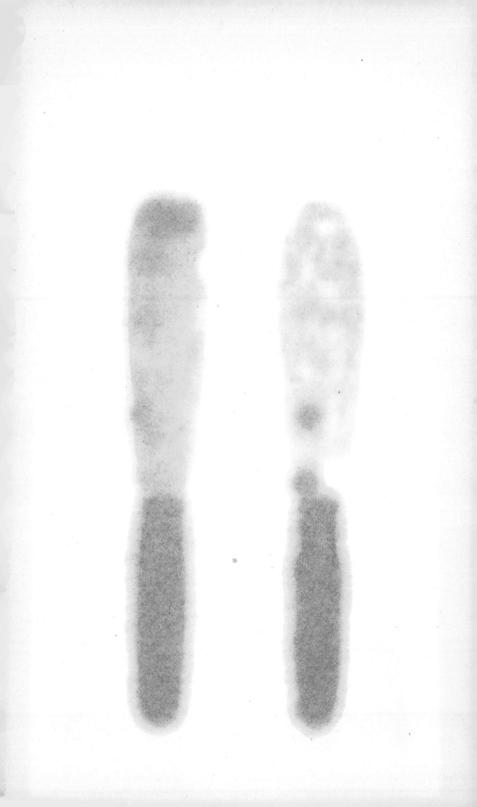

9/25/50